Scarlet and Black

STENDHAL

Level 6

Retold by Duncan Campbell-Smith
Series Editors: Andy Hopkins and Jocelyn Potter

English As A Second
Language Program

Pearson Education Limited
Edinburgh Gate, Harlow,
Essex CM20 2JE, England
and Associated Companies throughout the world.

ISBN 0 582 34368 2

Margaret R. B. Shaw's translation first published in Penguin Classics 1953
This edition first published 2000

Original copyright © Margaret R. B. Shaw 1953
Text copyright © Penguin Books 2000

Typeset by Ferdinand Pageworks, London
Set in 11/14pt Bembo
Printed in Spain by Mateu Cromo, S. A. Pinto (Madrid)

Published by Pearson Education Limited in association with
Penguin Books Ltd, both companies being subsidiaries of Pearson Plc

For a complete list of the titles available in the Penguin Readers series please write to your local
Pearson Education office or to: Marketing Department, Penguin Longman Publishing,
5 Bentinck Street, London W1M 5RN.

Contents

Introduction

So Julien took Mme de Rênal's hand and lifted it to his lips. She was astonished at his gesture and actually rather shocked. They looked at each other in silence for a moment before he let go of her hand. Seconds later she felt guilty that she had not reacted coldly, which would have been the proper response. Then her husband entered the hall, and the moment was past.

Julien Sorel is the son of a village peasant. Mme de Rênal is the beautiful wife of the local Mayor. Within a few moments of their first meeting, there is an immediate attraction between them despite their very different backgrounds, and this changes both their lives for ever. Their relationship, set in France about ten years after the defeat of Napoleon in 1815, is also the story of a young man who loses his way in a complex world. Julien is fiercely ambitious, and clever enough to rise quickly in society from a poor family background. His own strong emotions, though, threaten to wreck his plans from the start. And his love affair with Mme de Rênal is not exactly a cautious beginning.

The man who wrote *Scarlet and Black* in 1830 said more than once: 'Julien Sorel is myself.' Stendhal's real name was Henri Marie Beyle and he was born in France six years before the Revolution of 1789. When he was sixteen years old, he joined the army to fight under Napoleon, and he took part in several of Napoleon's most famous battles. After Napoleon was defeated in 1815, he went to live in Italy and became a writer using the name 'Stendhal'. He had various homes in Italy and in Paris for the rest of his life, but he was never able to settle properly in either place. He completed only four novels. *Scarlet and Black* is the second of them, and a classic of French literature.

Like Stendhal, the young hero of *Scarlet and Black* is never really able to find his place in the world. Unlike his creator, Julien is born too late to have a soldier's career – though, like many Frenchmen in the years after 1815, he believes he would happily have died fighting in the scarlet uniform of Napoleon's army. Instead, Julien accepts that he is most likely to succeed in life if he becomes a priest, forever dressed in black. The title of the book, *Scarlet and Black*, is a reference to these two uniforms.

Priests enjoyed great power and influence in France in the late 1820s. The church was a strong supporter of the royal family, which in 1815 had regained the position it had lost at the time of the French Revolution. On the other hand, many Frenchmen in the 1820s were republicans who strongly opposed the return of their royal family and hated those priests who supported it. The republicans were also bitter enemies of the church itself; they believed that it was based on political, not religious interests.

This is the background to Julien Sorel's personal story: France is a society deeply divided for political reasons. It is also divided, and just as deeply, by a system of social classes that define people by their family name as well as by the level of their income. Both sources of danger, political and social, threaten disaster for Julien as he makes his way in life from a small country town to the richest homes in Paris.

While this background contributes to the excitement of the story, however, the reputation of *Scarlet and Black* as a great novel comes above all from Stendhal's main characters and his analysis of their motives.

Mme de Rênal is a lady of the provinces, married to a boring man who takes little notice of her; Mathilde de la Mole is a Paris beauty, forced to spend every evening with dull young men who are only interested in gossip. Both feel trapped and desperate. Perhaps it is not surprising that both of them, faced with Julien's sudden arrival, decide he is everything they have been lacking in their lives. But what are *his* real motives for responding to them as he does? To what extent is he always calculating his next move? And when do events finally pass out of Julien's control?

Stendhal based *Scarlet and Black* on a true story that was reported in the Paris newspapers in 1827. He turned it into a novel that explored the psychology of human behaviour in ways that no novel had done before.

Chapter 1　A Humble Start

No one who has ever lived in a huge and busy city like Paris can ever visit a small country town without noticing how careful people are to behave correctly. People gossip constantly about what their neighbours are doing. Great care is needed to build and protect a reputation, especially in public life.

As Mayor of the pretty town of Verrières, in the lower slopes of the French Alps, Monsieur* de Rênal was very careful indeed. He always maintained the serious face that minor officials consider is appropriate to their position. He also had the benefit of a large private fortune. In the ten years since the defeat of Napoleon at Waterloo, Verrières had become a wealthy manufacturing centre, and M. de Rênal's business was the most successful in the town. He had a fine new house, built of newly cut stone. And in front of the house was a large garden, laid out with several walls around it. The whole design exactly matched the latest property fashions of those days. Every wall was a sign of success: and the more of them a man owned on his property, the more highly his neighbours respected him.

It was therefore fortunate for M. de Rênal's reputation that, during his time as Mayor, a huge supporting wall had been urgently needed by the town for a public path alongside the river that ran through Verrières. After making several visits to Paris to gain the necessary permission for this project, M. de Rênal had achieved its successful completion despite opposition from his Liberal opponents on the Verrières town council. The finished path offered a fine view of five or six valleys leading up into the

* Monsieur, Madame, Mademoiselle: the French words for Mr, Mrs and Miss. The short forms of these titles are M., Mme and Mlle.

mountains. M. de Rênal felt a proud man – even prouder than usual – whenever he walked along it with Madame de Rênal and their three young sons. And there, one fine autumn afternoon, he first mentioned to his wife the idea of appointing a tutor for their children.

He had not been enjoying this particular walk as much as usual. Earlier in the day he had had a bitter quarrel with the parish priest of Verrières, Father Chélan. The priest had given some help with local introductions to an official from Paris whom M. de Rênal suspected of plotting against his authority as Mayor. In the heat of their quarrel, M. de Rênal had dismissed Father Chélan as the village priest – even though he was eighty years old and had lived in Verrières for over half a century. To M. de Rênal's disgust, his dear wife now hardly seemed to understand why he had had to take this action.

'After all,' she said, 'what harm can this gentleman from Paris really do?'

This astonished M. de Rênal. To prevent himself losing his temper, he stopped and stared at their children – and this reminded him of his decision about a tutor.

'I have absolutely made up my mind,' he said suddenly, 'to take young Sorel, the carpenter's son, into my house. He will look after the children; they're beginning to be too noisy for us. I hear this young man is almost a priest already! He knows Latin well and has a strong character, I'm told. And besides, no one else in Verrières has a tutor to walk out with their children!'

Mme de Rênal smiled at her husband approvingly. She had a simple and trusting nature, and never questioned his ambitious plans for the future of their children. Instead, she urged him on.

'There are other people in this town,' she said, 'who might think of hiring this unusual young man before us if we delay too long.'

'All right, then, it's decided!' said M. de Rênal – and early the next morning he stepped out at six to present his proposal, that young Julien Sorel should join their household for a salary of three hundred francs a year.

Old Sorel senior lived with his family next to his own wood mill just a little way below M. de Rênal's greatly admired garden walls. Until some years before, in fact, the Sorel family had actually lived on land now enclosed by the walls: the Mayor of Verrières had had to pay the peasant Sorel a silly sum of money to move his house to its present site. It still annoyed M. de Rênal to recall that bargain, and the bitter memory of old Sorel publicly smiling over it, several months later. Other, happier matters were on the Mayor's mind this morning, though, as he found the carpenter busy measuring some pieces of timber on the path to his mill.

Old Sorel was very surprised and secretly delighted by the extraordinary offer that M. de Rênal put to him. His face remained as miserable as usual, though, which is always how these mountain peasants hide their cleverness. He replied by thanking the Mayor politely for several minutes, while he tried hard to hide his surprise. He himself was extremely disappointed in his youngest son. But here was the Mayor offering three hundred francs a year to hire the boy for his own household!

Old Sorel insisted that he could not accept the offer there and then: he pretended that he had to consult with his son. This of course thoroughly alarmed M. de Rênal, who immediately remembered his wife's warning and worried that a better offer had indeed come from elsewhere. But he had no choice. He would have to wait until the next day for his answer.

As soon as the Mayor had gone, Old Sorel hurried across to his mill and called out for Julien. There was no sign of him anywhere, only his two older brothers hard at work preparing pine trees for the mill.

Old Sorel went into the mill and looked around angrily for

the missing boy. Then he saw him – sitting in the beams of the roof, busy reading a book! Nothing could have made the old man more angry. He could forgive the boy his weak body, but how he hated this crazy passion for reading! He himself could not read.

He called out two or three times, but Julien could not hear him over the noise of the mill. In the end, in spite of his age, Old Sorel jumped up across the tree logs and into the roof beams. A violent blow sent the book in Julien's hand flying down into the river below; another blow, as violent as the first and this time aimed at his head, made the boy lose his balance. He would have fallen three or four metres down into the levers of the mill's machinery below if his father's left hand had not caught him and held him back.

As soon as the two of them had returned safely to the ground, Old Sorel pushed his son roughly towards the house.

'God knows what he's going to do to me now,' thought the boy to himself.

As he passed beside the river, he looked sadly down into the water where his book had fallen. It was his favourite book of all, *A Memoir of St Helena* – one of thirty or forty titles given to him by an old army doctor. The doctor, now dead, had settled in Verrières after serving under Napoleon in the Italian battles of 1796. Julien had loved the old fellow dearly and learned from him all the Latin and history he knew (or in other words, all the history of the Italian battles of 1796). How different things were now! He hated his own father, and had very few friends left in Verrières. Every Sunday, when games were played in the town square, he was chased and hit by his brothers and all their friends.

He expected more violence as his father pulled him into the house. Instead, though, the old peasant turned and began to shout fiercely in his face.

'I'll never know how you managed to arrange this with Mme

de Rênal! But I don't care because I'll be rid of you anyway. She wants you to look after her children. God knows why! So you can leave this house, and my mill will run more smoothly when you do!'

Julien was amazed. He struggled to understand what was happening to him, as his father went on shouting and then rushed out of the house to consult with his other two sons.

Father and son ignored each other for the rest of the day. In the evening, Julien went as usual for his lesson in bible studies with Father Chélan; but neither the priest nor his pupil spoke of the sudden change in their circumstances.

◆

Early the next morning, M. de Rênal sent for Old Sorel. The peasant kept the Mayor waiting for two hours, but arrived full of polite apologies. Then the two of them began to discuss their bargain. It was quickly apparent that M. de Rênal was eager to reach agreement, which of course only encouraged Old Sorel to think of one difficulty after another. He wanted to be assured that his son would have his meals with the Mayor and his wife; that he would sleep in a fine room with the three children; that he would have a smart new black suit to wear.

They argued for more than two hours – until at last the clever tricks of the peasant overcame the clever tricks of the rich man (who did not have to depend on clever tricks for his daily bread). Then the deal was done, and Julien Sorel was appointed tutor to the de Rênal household at a salary of four hundred francs a year (plus a smart black suit that he could keep even if the appointment was not a success).

When he returned to his mill, Old Sorel at first could not find his youngest son: Julien had left the house in the middle of the night. Worried about what might happen to them, he had taken all his books to hide them in the house of a childhood friend,

Fouqué, who lived high up in the mountains above the town. Coming back at midday, he found his father purple with anger.

'You lazy little pig!' shouted Old Sorel. 'I doubt you will ever pay me back for all the food I've fed you over the years! But take all your rubbish with you and move to the Mayor's. I've no use for a tutor as a son: they can have you!'

Julien grabbed his few possessions and hurried away. As soon as he was out of his father's sight, though, he stopped to rest for a second. Then the idea came to him that he should pray for some moments before beginning his new life, and he walked slowly to the town church.

Sitting alone in the darkness of the church, he thought about his future and everything he had already done to prepare for it. As a child, he had always wanted to be a soldier dressed in a scarlet uniform. As his friend the army doctor had predicted, though, things were different now. These days the Church, not the army, was the real power in France. So Julien had stopped talking of Napoleon and decided to become a priest. Some priests, after all, now earned three times the salary of one of Napoleon's generals! Gifted with rare powers of memory and fiercely ambitious, he saw the church as his path to success – which above all, at the age of eighteen, meant escaping from Verrières.

He was just going to leave when he noticed on the seat beside him a dirty piece of paper, lying flat as if it was meant to be read. On it he saw the following words: *Details of the last moments and death of Louis Jenrel, guillotined at Besançon on . . .*

'Who could have put this paper there?' thought Julien. 'Poor fellow!' he whispered to himself. 'His name ends just like mine . . .' and he threw away the paper.

As he walked to the door of the church, Julien imagined he saw some blood in a small hole in the stone floor. In fact it was only some holy water, spilt by one of the priests: the reflection in the water of a red curtain over a window made it appear to be a small pool of blood. For a moment Julien felt a secret terror about what this might mean. Then he was ashamed.

'Am I a coward, after all?' he said to himself.

He hurried to the door and marched quickly off towards M. de Rênal's house.

Chapter 2   The Gifted Tutor

Mme de Rênal was just stepping out of a side-door into the garden when she noticed an obviously shy young peasant boy at the gate. For nearly two days she had been worrying terribly about the plan to bring a tutor into the house. No doubt he would be a rough, smelly man, and it would be his duty to punish her children severely every time they failed to pass a test of their Latin grammar. She never guessed for a moment that this pale creature at the gate could be her husband's choice! Always of a romantic nature, she could almost imagine it was a young woman in disguise, coming to beg a favour from the Mayor.

Julien did not see her approaching from the side of the house. He gave a little jump when a gentle voice said close to his ear: 'What brings you here, my boy?'

Turning to find Mme de Rênal before him, he was astonished at her beauty and immediately forgot everything, even why he had come at all. Mme de Rênal had to repeat her question.

'I've come here as tutor, madam,' he said to her at last.

Then it was her turn to be lost for words. Though certainly pale and very thin, Julien had big, dark eyes. As young women in the town had been beginning to notice for some time, in fact, he was extraordinarily good-looking. A sense of relief flooded over Mme de Rênal: she could hardly believe the contrast between what she had feared and what she now saw before her.

'Shall we go in, sir?' she said to him in some embarrassment.

7

Julien followed her into the hall, amazed to have been addressed as 'sir' by such a rich and beautiful woman. She asked him a few formal questions about himself, and especially his knowledge of Latin, in a sweet tone of voice that she hoped would give him courage. She was going to be surprised. As they talked, the bold idea occurred to Julien to kiss her hand. Half of him was frightened at the thought. A moment later he was telling himself that he would be a coward not to do it: it would certainly suggest to this fine lady that he was more than just a humble peasant from the mill . . .

So Julien took Mme de Rênal's hand and lifted it to his lips. She was astonished at his gesture and actually rather shocked. They looked at each other in silence for a moment before he let go of her hand. Seconds later she felt guilty that she had not reacted coldly, which would have been the proper response. Then her husband entered the hall, and the moment was past.

M. de Rênal led Julien off to talk about the conditions of his employment, and the two of them soon left the house to visit the town in search of a black suit for Julien. So it was some hours later before the de Rênal children met their tutor for the first time.

What happened next amazed the children and everyone else. Julien handed one of them a tiny black book.

'This is the Holy Bible,' he told the oldest child. 'Open it where you like and read the first words of any paragraph. I will tell you the rest of the page without looking!'

And so he did, not once but again and again. He had memorized the whole of the New Testament.★

The family servants were soon gathering at the door to witness this marvellous skill, while M. de Rênal stared proudly around the room. That evening, his house attracted dozens of

★ New Testament: the second section of the Holy Bible, which deals with the life and teachings of Jesus.

curious visitors, which did the Mayor's general reputation no harm at all. Julien repeated his trick many times – this was something he had been training to do for years. In truth, though, it very soon annoyed him to see how easily he could amuse all these rich people. Any of them could have afforded to buy him a proper education without noticing the cost. But he pretended to enjoy the attention, and went on performing.

◆

In many ways, this was the story of the next several months. The children loved Julien and he made a very good tutor. For most households in Verrières, as everywhere else in the provinces of the 1820s, life was horribly boring. Julien's presence in the de Rênal household provided a constant source of interest and excitement.

Despite the fact that his salary was increased as a result, though, Julien secretly hated his new life. He sometimes had to struggle hard to hide the disgust that he felt for the Mayor and his friends, who talked only about business and money. He couldn't bear the polite dinner parties, where everyone made fun of Napoleon and the old days of the Republic, and all the talk of honesty when every man was quietly plotting to rob his neighbours.

Julien, however, was not the only person in the household with feelings that had to be hidden. Little by little, Mme de Rênal found herself falling in love with this extraordinary young man ten years younger than herself.

It took her some months to realize this. Of course, you may say it was obvious from the start what would happen. In Paris, Mme de Rênal herself would certainly have known what to expect. But in Paris love is always encouraged by literature, and half a dozen novels would have warned her of her future, and Julien's too.

Under the cold grey skies of Verrières, by contrast, it was inevitably a different story. She simply saw herself as a respectable lady of thirty years of age, busy looking after her children and not interested at all in copying the plot of a novel – even when she was faced with the arrival of this romantic young man. Everything happens gradually in the provinces; and everything is more natural there.

Soon after his arrival in the house, Mme de Rênal began to worry about Julien's obvious poverty. How very much she wished that she could do something to help him! She was, after all, the heiress of a wealthy, unmarried aunt. When she tried one day to offer him a gift, however, Julien refused it so rudely that poor Mme de Rênal was quite shocked. So there was no way for her to express her tender feelings towards him; and if they found themselves walking together with the children, they usually walked in silence. Or else Julien talked about what doctors did in Napoleon's army, which was worse.

Those tender feelings, though, continued to grow. The first crisis came when the Mayor's household servant, Elisa, announced to Mme de Rênal that she herself had fallen in love with Julien. More than that, she had actually asked him to marry her and to share in a small sum of money that her parents had left to her.

This news caused Mme de Rênal to become so excited that she almost fell ill. Then, later that same day, Elisa announced that Julien had refused her. She cried sadly all evening – but Mme de Rênal was so overcome with relief that she actually fainted. When Julien appeared at dinner, she turned bright red and had to leave the room, complaining of a headache.

'That's like all you women,' said M. de Rênal, roaring with laughter. 'Such little machines are always in need of repair.'

♦

Spring arrived, and the unsuspecting Mayor moved his wife and family to a summer house in Vergy, a pretty village in the hills above Verrières. (The royal family moved to the country for the summer, so the de Rênal family had to do the same.) Here, while the Mayor spent frequent periods away in Verrières on business, Mme de Rênal and Julien discovered a shared passion for wild flowers. So now they had plenty to talk about. Soon they were spending hours together every day, talking and laughing endlessly, though always about very innocent things. Suddenly Elisa was being asked to prepare clean dresses two or three times a day.

And Julien? He was happier than ever before. He had no enemies, no violent brothers and no fierce father chasing him. Between his lessons with the children, he could do almost as he pleased from one day to the next. The result would not have surprised his father: he spent more and more of his time reading. And, as always, the books he loved best told stories of Napoleon – still his real hero.

As he was reading one day about Napoleon's success with ladies, and his hero's bold approach to matters of the heart, something occurred to Julien that any other young man would have thought about long before. He would have to seduce Mme de Rênal! As soon as the idea came to him, it became almost a duty. He could think about nothing else. But how could it be done?

The answer, he soon realized, was to take advantage of the long hot summer evenings that had now arrived. He passed most of them sitting and talking in the garden with Mme de Rênal and any guests staying in the house – usually her cousin, Mme Derville. Julien decided that the next evening, when no one was watching, he would take Mme de Rênal's hand and hold it tightly until she agreed to leave it in his grasp.

Conversation the next evening was not easy. The sky was

heavy and seemed to threaten a storm. Julien promised himself that he would act as the clock struck ten – and so he did. Mme de Rênal pulled her hand quickly away.

Without knowing very well what he was doing, Julien seized hold of it a second time, and pressed it hard. She made a last attempt to pull it away from him, but in the end this hand remained in his. A little later, as the storm winds gathered, a flower pot fell over and Mme de Rênal jumped to pick it up. But she had hardly sat down again before she let him take her hand in his once more, as if it was something agreed on between them.

Midnight passed: they had to leave the garden and separate for the night. Mme de Rênal, full of passion, lay awake all night with happiness. Julien slept like a log.

So well, indeed, that he slept late the next morning and was late for the children's first lesson. When their father arrived from Verrières just before lunch, he did not hide his annoyance over Julien's increasingly relaxed attitude to his work. In fact, M. de Rênal quite openly insulted his children's tutor. This was too much for Julien. With the passing of every month of that summer at Vergy, he had come to hate his wealthy master, and all his business friends, with a growing passion. The Mayor of Verrières was by now the representative, in his eyes, of all the unfairly rich and powerful men on earth.

'Sir,' said Julien, suddenly mad with anger, 'do you believe your children would have made the same progress with any other tutor? If your answer is no,' he went on without giving M. de Rênal time to reply, 'how dare you complain that I pay them too little attention?'

The Mayor could hardly believe his ears. He was certainly going to lose his temper, when it occurred to him that Julien must have received the offer of another job elsewhere. Even from one of his business competitors! This was a disaster he had to avoid at all costs.

'I am very sorry to see you so upset,' said M. de Rênal. He laughed nervously while the young man stared back at him. 'Very well, sir,' he added after a long pause, 'I will give you what you ask: from the day after tomorrow, I will pay you fifty francs a month.'

Julien stood there simply astonished, seized with a desire to laugh. The children, who had been listening to the whole scene, ran past to look for their mother in the garden. Out of habit, Julien followed them without even a glance at M. de Rênal, who was left feeling very annoyed. Then he ran off into the fields and shouted out to the sky to release all his mixed emotions.

'I've won a battle,' he said to himself in amazement. 'I've really won a battle! I can deceive the old fool with his wife and chase him for more money as well!'

At this same moment, though, the children were telling their mother about all that had happened. The news affected her deeply, and she spent a miserable afternoon waiting for Julien's return and hoping for an apology from him. Instead, things got much worse. The servant, Elisa, told her that she knew for certain that Julien had declared his love to a girl in Verrières.

It was a silly story invented by Elisa – but poor Mme de Rênal was overcome with jealousy. How bitterly she now regretted that she had allowed Julien to behave so inappropriately! She ran to her room and cried there for most of the night. Earlier that day she had been so happy, but now she felt guilty and ashamed. She had no idea that anyone could suffer so cruelly.

Eventually Elisa came to her and sat reading her a newspaper aloud to help comfort her. While she half-listened to Elisa, Mme de Rênal decided what to do. She made up her mind that, in all of her future dealings with Julien, she would treat him with complete and absolute coldness.

Chapter 3   Pleasures of a Private World

By the time Mme de Rênal rose next morning, Julien had already persuaded her husband to allow him three days of holiday from Vergy. He was keen to see Mme de Rênal again before he left, though, and he walked in the garden waiting for her to come down. She saw him from her window.

'Now,' she said to herself, 'is the moment to be strong!'

She stepped down to the garden, where Julien greeted her with a cheerful smile. She replied as coldly as she could: and his smile immediately disappeared.

Suddenly all the meaningless phrases we use in the mornings about the weather and our health were of no use to either of them. Both struggled to find anything at all to say. Julien felt angry: she was making him feel like a servant, and deliberately too! But he was clever enough to pretend that it did not worry him. So without even mentioning his plan to leave for a few days, he bowed stiffly and walked off.

Poor Mme de Rênal felt miserable, and there was more bad news for her a moment later. One of the children ran up to her and screamed happily: 'We've got a holiday! M. Julien is going away!'

The words filled her with horror, and regret for the way she had spoken to Julien. She was still worrying about this hours later when she sat down for lunch with her cousin and her husband. It did not improve her mood when she then heard M. de Rênal wondering aloud at the table whether Julien had left them to join another family.

'That young man is playing with my patience,' said the Mayor. He watched his wife withdraw from the table, clearly very upset about something. 'That's just like a woman!' he said. 'Always something going wrong in these complicated machines!' And he went off laughing quietly to himself.

Julien, meanwhile, was a long way away, riding to the home of his friend Fouqué. He did not go straight there: high in the mountains, he stopped at a small cave. There he sat alone for some hours, thinking of the life he was determined to make for himself.

'One day,' he thought, 'I will live in Paris – and there I will have all the rewards of a successful career as either a soldier or a priest, whichever offers me the better chances. And I will enjoy the love of a woman far more beautiful and passionate than any woman in the provinces could ever be!'

It was the middle of the night by the time he reached his friend's house. Fouqué was still awake, though, hard at work on the accounts of his business in the timber trade. In the next three days, Julien heard a lot about this business, and also about Fouqué's busy love life. The business conversations did not interest him much. Fouqué thought they should work together as partners – he had always greatly respected his friend's cleverness. But Julien did not intend to spend years of his life earning a safe and steady income at the price of abandoning all his ambitious dreams of Paris. Fouqué's love life, full of secret affairs and betrayed promises, was much more entertaining.

♦

Fouqué's stories were so entertaining, in fact, that Julien rode back to Vergy thinking for the first time about the possibility of actually having a full sexual affair with Mme de Rênal. If he was honest with himself, he would have preferred the idea of sex with her cousin. But it seemed likely that Mme Derville already knew that something was going on between himself and Mme de Rênal, so Julien ignored that idea.

An affair with Mme de Rênal, on the other hand – that looked a distinct possibility. After his return to Vergy, it was obvious to Julien that she was desperate to know his plans for the future. All her efforts to treat Julien more coolly were forgotten, as she delighted in his return. So Julien made up his mind: he would plot to become nothing less than Mme de Rênal's lover.

Sure now of success, and every day growing more ambitious, Julien moved quickly. First he declared to Mme de Rênal that he was passionately in love with her. (This sent her away as happy as a lamb.) Next morning he suddenly gave her a first kiss as they walked from one room of the house to another. (This alarmed Mme de Rênal, who found a moment to say to Julien: 'I must order you to be careful.') And the next evening, as the two of them were sitting in the garden after dinner, he leaned over and whispered into her ear: 'Madam, tonight at two I will come to your room. There's something I must say to you.'

This last move genuinely amazed Mme de Rênal. She replied so quietly that Julien could hardly catch all her words, but they certainly included, 'You ought to be ashamed.' And perhaps he was, since Julien soon left her sitting with her cousin Mme Derville, and went off to his bed feeling very miserable and even a little silly.

He found it impossible to sleep, of course: second thoughts about his awkward behaviour just went round and round in his brain until he was quite exhausted. And at that point, the clock of Vergy church struck two. The hour of his big test had come. Julien was not lacking in courage as he climbed from his bed.

'I may be the son of a peasant, as Mme Derville keeps reminding me,' he said to himself, 'but at least I won't be weak!'

Then he had to lean against the wall to stay upright, on trembling knees.

He crept out of his bedroom and along the corridor past M. de Rênal's door, where the sound of heavy breathing robbed Julien of his best excuse for giving up the whole idea. Then, without knowing what he would do when he arrived there, he pushed open the door to Mme de Rênal's bedroom and stepped inside.

She saw him enter, and leapt out of bed with a shout. This

alarmed him so much that he completely forgot whatever useless plans he had. He fell at her feet, grabbing her knees. Then, as she continued abusing him for being in her room, he burst into tears. It was not a trick; but nothing could have been better planned to sweep away Mme de Rênal's defences. She took him in her arms and covered him with kisses . . .

When Julien left Mme de Rênal's room a few hours later, it might be said, to adopt the language of novels, that he had nothing more to wish for.

And so a truly passionate affair began. Mme de Rênal soon lost all her worries that Julien might turn against her as a result of her age – she was, after all, ten years older than him. She experienced a happiness that she had never known before. Julien found himself no longer plotting an affair just in order to pursue his ambitions. He was actually in love with Mme de Rênal for her own sake.

His career ambitions were never far from his mind – which might have caused some concern to a woman with more experience of men than Mme de Rênal had had. But he lost all his fear of being treated by her as her social inferior. Julien had never known the love of anyone before in his life. How strange but thrilling it was, to feel able to trust another human being so completely! Suddenly he wanted to share everything with Mme de Rênal, even his most secret thoughts.

This almost led to disaster. As the two of them were sitting alone talking in the garden one evening, Julien suddenly mentioned for the first time how much he admired the past achievements of Napoleon. He especially appreciated the opportunities that Napoleon had created for young men with a good education but no family wealth behind them.

'Ah, what a tragedy for those men that he is gone!' he cried.

Mme de Rênal went white. 'We do not mix any more with people of that sort,' she said in an icy tone.

Napoleon, and every story about him, filled her with horror. And young men educated above their position in society were, according to her husband's friends, the kind of people who would bring back the Revolution. She preferred to pretend that the Revolution had never happened. Generally, in fact, she wanted to view the world only as a place full of people as rich as she was. Her manner towards Julien remained cold for some moments after his remarks.

Julien saw his mistake immediately. He never mentioned Napoleon at Vergy again – but nor did he ever again abandon himself so completely to his love for Mme de Rênal. She belonged to a society that Julien could never join, he realized better than before. Deep in his soul, Julien stood outside her world. He understood that now.

They remained lovers, however. In fact, perhaps because of this incident, Mme de Rênal even began to teach him about the local politics of Verrières. It was all part of the general education that she wanted to give him. This was her way of helping him to become a great man. She was certain that a noble future, perhaps at the head of the King's army or of the Church in France, was Julien's real destination in life.

♦

As it happened, Julien had a taste of both the army and the Church in the next few weeks. It was announced that the King of France would be passing through Verrières on a royal tour of the region, and various grand ceremonies had to be arranged by M. de Rênal in honour of his visit.

Two were particularly important – a march through the town by a military guard of honour, and a special religious service in a historic church a few kilometres outside Verrières. M. de Rênal's wife insisted that Julien should ride in the guard of honour. She was determined to see him dressed in a scarlet uniform for once, in place of his usual black tutor's clothes. The second ceremony involved Julien because his old bible teacher, Father Chélan, was in charge of arranging the service and demanded that Julien should be his assistant. In the end, the young man performed his duties well in both roles (though some who attended the church service noticed that bits of a soldier's uniform were strangely visible under the clothing of one of the priests).

Of the two, the church service impressed Julien more. Of course he enjoyed riding in uniform and imagining himself in the army of Napoleon, attacking a gun position. But he had never seen the tremendous power and social influence of the men of the church in action before, and he was simply overcome. It was exciting and extraordinary – and he could see himself a part of it.

Among the good citizens of Verrières, less happily, the bigger sensation had been caused by the sight of Julien in a uniform and on a horse. Many wealthy families in the town were disgusted that the Mayor had allowed a peasant's son to join the guard of honour. And why had this been allowed? Everyone thought they knew the answer. The gossip that followed was not kind to Mme de Rênal.

◆

Mme de Rênal and Julien were increasingly aware of the risks that they were taking. More than once, she tried to break off the affair. When her eldest son fell dangerously ill, for example, she saw it as a warning from God and begged Julien to leave the house. But he knew that the moment he left, she would confess everything to her husband. All of them would be ruined. So he stayed, the son recovered – and the love affair continued.

Mme Derville had long ago abandoned her cousin and left Vergy, sure that a scandal was approaching. And what she had noticed, the servants could see plainly every day.

Mme de Rênal's own servant, Elisa, went to Verrières one morning to attend to some small legal business that concerned her. In the town she met one of the Mayor's political rivals, a nasty fellow called M. Valenod. He spoke angrily to her about Julien's part in the King's visit.

'You'd get me into trouble, sir, if I told you the truth,' said Elisa. 'We poor servants are never forgiven for speaking out about certain things . . .'

After M. Valenod had cleverly cut short all these polite excuses, he learned certain things that were deeply upsetting to his pride. He could hardly believe it! This grand lady, whom he himself had spent so many years of his youth chasing with every attention, had actually taken a young peasant for her lover!

'And M. Julien really didn't make much of an effort to win her, either,' said Elisa helpfully.

That evening, M. de Rênal received from the town, with his daily newspaper, a long letter with no signature at the end. It informed him in the fullest detail of what was happening in his own house. Julien, from the other side of the table, saw the Mayor grow pale as he read it.

Chapter 4   A Painful Parting

The Mayor only stayed pale for a short time. Then he turned very red. His eyes went blank as he stared at the paper in his hands, and his hands began to shake. Julien, watching closely, guessed immediately what had happened and slipped quickly away from the table. He just managed to speak to Mme de Rênal as she was walking to her bedroom.

'Let's not meet tonight,' said Julien. 'I am certain that your husband's letter is an unsigned poison-pen letter! Anyway, he definitely suspects something!'

Julien quickly left for bed himself, and locked his bedroom door. An hour or two later, he was glad he had done so. He heard someone approach the door and try to enter. Was it his lover or a jealous husband? Julien held his breath, until he heard the footsteps returning back down the corridor.

In fact it was poor Mme de Rênal, desperate to see Julien. She was afraid that he had only invented the letter story to avoid making love to her that night. Back in her own room, though, she began to have second thoughts. She started to realize the full implications of a really revealing letter.

'Thank Heavens,' she thought, 'for Julien's quick thinking!'

Early next morning, Julien found a note from her pushed beneath his bedroom door. It started with one appeal after another for Julien to love her and never leave her. But it also contained a brilliant idea to deal with the problem of an enemy's letter that might have betrayed them.

She told Julien that they had to assume that her husband had guessed correctly. The only escape for them now would be another poison-pen letter. Julien himself would have to write this, and Mme de Rênal could pretend she had been given it in the town.

This second letter would be just as nasty as the first, and would accuse her of all sorts of things: she told Julien what it should say. If he could give it to her later that morning, she would then hand it over to her husband with disgust and ask for his help. This would completely confuse him, she was sure. Especially because – and this was the really clever part of the plan – the letter could be constructed by Julien from pieces of old letters sent to her years ago by the Mayor's great rival, M. Valenod . . .

While the two lovers were working all this out, M. de Rênal himself was close to planning a murder, perhaps even two. From the moment he had opened the letter, his brain had begun to spin. Absolutely miserable and full of self-pity, he also felt that he was the loneliest man in the world. He had no close friends, he realized, to whom he could turn for help at his time of need. All night he had lain awake, thinking over his past life. Ah, why had he betrayed so many personal friends for the sake of his reputation as a small-town politician! But his anger with himself soon turned to thoughts of revenge.

'By God, I can surprise this young peasant with my wife and kill them both,' said M. de Rênal to himself, marching up and down his bedroom as the first light of dawn appeared in the sky.

He took down his hunting knife. It was very sharp indeed, but the thought of blood frightened him. For the next few hours, he struggled to decide how much public shame he could bear to live with. And which would be worse – a couple of murders in the family, or the revelation one day that his wife had run away to Paris with their tutor?

By the end of the morning, he was walking like a ghost in the garden. Just as he was thinking how he might most easily catch Julien and his wife together and murder them both, he walked round a corner of the garden path . . . and straight into his wife.

She handed him a letter, clearly opened already but carefully folded again. He looked at his wife without reading it, a mad look in his eyes.

'Just look at this disgusting thing,' said Mme de Rênal. 'Some rough fellow handed it to me as I was leaving the church service this morning. One thing's quite obvious: we have to get rid of M. Julien immediately! We must send him back to his family.'

What a thrill it was to see the effect of her words on M. de Rênal! She knew immediately that Julien had guessed correctly – and that she had found the right solution. Her husband stared in shock at this second letter, with all its words and phrases consisting of little bits of paper cut up and stuck together.

'I think I'm going crazy!' screamed the Mayor, marching off down the path.

A few seconds later, though, he came marching back again and seemed much calmer.

'We've really got to dismiss Julien,' his wife announced again, before he could utter a word. 'He's a clever boy and I'm sure he'll be able to get another position with one of the families in town – like M. Valenod's family, perhaps.'

'Spoken just like the silly woman you are!' shouted M. de Rênal, trembling with emotion. 'But why expect good sense from a woman? Your shallow, idle minds are only happy running around looking for wild flowers! You're all so weak and emotional!'

There was much, much more like this for several moments. Mme de Rênal let him go on talking, while she kept a cool head and calculated her best next moves. As soon as she got the chance, she dropped a clever hint about an affair between M. Valenod and their servant Elisa. This stopped her husband in mid-sentence. Then she referred, quite quietly, to a pile of letters she had actually once received herself from M. Valenod.

'Show me these letters at once, I command it!' shouted M. de Rênal, with as much authority as he could manage. Mme de Rênal pretended to be shocked at the idea of him seeing them, and began to make excuses for keeping them private. Predictably, this made her husband even angrier. Finally, she confessed that the letters were locked up in her private desk – and watched, amazed, as M. de Rênal ran off to her room with an iron bar in his hands.

By the time she reached him there, the desk was broken open and his fingers were tearing at the little pile of letters. Mme de Rênal was now growing increasingly bold. As soon as she had the chance to be heard, she urged again that Julien should be dismissed as soon as possible.

'Every day he's growing a little more unprofessional, constantly praising me with fine words borrowed from some awful novel or other . . .'

'But he never reads any!' shouted M. de Rênal. 'I've made sure that. Do you think I'm the sort of master who's blind to everything and doesn't know what's going on in his own home?'

Then suddenly he stopped. There was a moment of total silence.

'Aha!' he cried, and threw the letters from M. Valenod down on to the desk, which he banged so hard with his fist that the whole room shook. 'Your poison-pen letter and these letters from Valenod! They're both written on exactly the same paper!'

'At last!' thought Mme de Rênal, with relief.

She let her mouth drop open in surprise. From this moment, though, she knew the battle was won. Because of his hatred of M. Valenod, her husband could hardly doubt her innocence.

His first thought was to go straight to M. Valenod's house. She quickly discouraged him. Would it not be a terrible mistake, she asked, to risk any talk at all about scandals in the de Rênal household? So, little by little, M. de Rênal was shown the wisdom of ignoring the poison-pen letters. It would require courage and real wisdom, his wife cleverly suggested.

'Very true,' said the Mayor, making up his mind to do nothing after all.

Even then, as everyone does in the provinces, he went on talking for quite a long time, repeating all his arguments several times. Finally, two hours of useless talk exhausted the strength of a man who had been awake all night. He decided at last to ignore both the letters they had received.

To deceive her husband completely, though, Mme de Rênal had to play one last card. She had to insist that Julien should leave Vergy for a time and stay by himself in the family house in Verrières.

And so it was agreed: Julien left Mme de Rênal with the children at Vergy and moved back to the town.

♦

At first, this arrangement seemed to work well enough. The children visited their tutor for lessons several times a week. Mme de Rênal was able to relax a little after the scare over the mystery letter, and still found plenty of opportunities to spend time alone with Julien in Verrières. Even Julien was happy with the new arrangements. He enjoyed having more time to visit his old teacher Father Chélan, or to read and be alone with his books.

He was not, though, in any danger of being lonely: he soon found himself almost a guest of honour in one wealthy home after another. Everyone knew of his special talent, and he was constantly invited to parties so that, at the end of the evening, guests could hear him quote long passages from the bible from memory.

All this, however, quickly became another source of concern to M. de Rênal, who began to hear rumours that Julien might leave his job to work for another family. The Mayor was especially worried by a rumour that the wife of his bitter rival, M. Valenod, was planning to offer Julien the role of tutor to her children.

Now this was true: she was. But the idea was hardly likely to win the approval of M. Valenod himself. This charming gentleman had other ideas in mind, when it came to Julien Sorel.

Fiercely ambitious one day to replace M. de Rênal and become the Mayor himself, M. Valenod missed no opportunity to hurt the man who was officially his boss. As the man responsible for the day-to-day management of the town council's business, he was much more active than M. de Rênal. He was always busy around the town – writing, talking, ignoring any kind of rejection, but carefully avoiding any appearance of being personally self-important. He was also a deeply nasty man. He had surrounded himself on the council with stupid men who would never challenge his authority, and now spent hours every week plotting his own political advancement with senior members of the local clergy.

This was the reason why he had quickly given in to the pleasure of writing his unsigned letter to M. de Rênal weeks before. The fact that Julien was now living separately from Mme de Rênal was not going to stop M. Valenod encouraging the gossip about his rival's wife.

In fact, as the summer passed into autumn, it grew easier by the day for M. Valenod to spread damaging stories about the Mayor and his family. M. de Rênal had spent much of the summer on a property deal in Verrières that upset many of his neighbours. Let us not bore ourselves with the details of this business: but as a result of them, the whole town was now very happy to talk about the love affair between his wife and the carpenter's son.

♦

October arrived. The country house at Vergy was closed for the winter. The family moved back to Verrières – and very soon M. de Rênal was painfully aware of the hottest gossip in the town. In less than a week, all those serious people who enjoy delivering bad news – almost to compensate themselves for being so dull and responsible the rest of the time – were telling M. de Rênal of the cruellest suspicions. At the same time, of course, they explained away everything with their usual good manners.

It was all too much for the servant, Elisa. She had left the de Rênal household months before and had been found a new position in Verrières by M. Valenod. This young woman now thought of the excellent idea of confessing her sins the next Sunday to Father Chélan – and at the same time giving him a detailed account of Julien's love affair.

Father Chélan sent for Julien as the church bell was striking six the following morning.

'I'm not asking you,' he said, 'I'm begging – and if necessary ordering – you to say nothing, and to go immediately to the seminary at Besançon. You must leave Verrières and not come back for a year.'

Then he told Julien of all the arrangements that he had personally made for him to go to Besançon, a large military town seventy kilometres away. There the Church had one if its more famous seminaries, which trained young men to become priests.

The meeting lasted three hours. At last Julien left the priest's house and ran to warn Mme de Rênal. He found her in a state of despair. She had heard all the rumours herself, and already knew that they would have to separate. Holding back her tears with great difficulty, though, she was hugely relieved to see that Julien's love for her was genuine. He really was desperate at the idea of leaving! This gave her the strength to behave with a simple calm that affected Julien deeply.

M. de Rênal came into the house shortly afterwards. He was extremely angry at another poison-pen letter. It was more than he could bear. The natural weakness of his character – and a terrible fear that his wife, if accused by him again, might leave him and retire on her family's money to another part of France – had made him decide to consider her completely innocent. So now he would take action.

'I will take this letter to the town hall and show everyone it comes from that cheap gangster Valenod!' he shouted. 'I will shame him publicly, then I will challenge him to a duel!'

Then he left the house alone, went to the town's gun shop to buy two pistols and had them loaded.

'Good Lord,' thought Mme de Rênal, 'I might become a widow!' But the next moment she said to herself, 'If I don't prevent this duel, as I certainly can, then I shall be guilty of murdering my husband!'

It was clear what had to be done – and that afternoon she did it. She sat down with her husband for four long hours, and persuaded him in the end to offer Julien six hundred francs to go away and study in Besançon. This, she said, would be an even more courageous act than fighting M. Valenod in a duel. It was not so hard for M. de Rênal to believe this, since it always caused him great pain to lose a large sum of money.

To his great delight, when the time came for their parting, Julien actually refused to accept the money. M. de Rênal, with tears in his eyes, kissed the young man and wished him a safe journey.

◆

M. de Rênal did not know that Julien returned secretly three nights later to say one last goodbye to his wife. It was a terrible moment for poor Mme de Rênal. The two lovers sat for hours in the darkness, but she could hardly respond to Julien at all. Fear and grief took her voice away.

'Nobody could possibly feel more unhappy . . . I wish I could die . . . I feel my heart turning to ice . . .' These were the longest replies that Julien could get from her.

When dawn arrived, she stood and wiped away her tears.

'I'm sorry you can't kiss the children goodbye,' she said, turning her face away.

Julien left the house in a state of shock at her sadness. Before riding over the mountains, and for as long as he could see the tower of the church in Verrières, he kept turning round to look back in her direction.

Chapter 5   The Seminary

Julien spent a night with his friend Fouqué, who lent him some money and some clothes, then rode on across the mountains to Besançon. Besançon was one of the prettiest towns in France, built within powerful castle walls. It was still an important base for the French army.

'It would be so different for me,' thought Julien, 'if I was entering this town as an army officer in charge of its defence!'

The reality was very different, of course. He was entering as a poor peasant's son, with not much money and no useful connections except an introductory letter from Father Chélan to the head of the seminary, Father Pirard.

Perhaps this was not quite true: a handsome face and a great charm were of rather more value in a town like Besançon than they had been in Verrières. Julien soon discovered this, in a café where he went for some lunch. The waitress was a real beauty, with a very good figure and dressed in a manner that guaranteed the café plenty of business. She felt sorry for Julien, who clearly knew nothing of the world, and in no time the two were flirting with each other quite openly.

Unfortunately for Julien, the waitress already had a lover who, only about ten minutes later, arrived by chance at the café. The waitress only just managed to persuade Julien to avoid a fight, and he left promising to see her again another day. (He never did.)

After this exciting start, what a terrible moment it was when he arrived a few hours later at the door of the seminary! The place looked like a prison.

'Why did I ever agree to come here?' thought Julien in despair.

He had to wait for ten minutes at the door before anyone even answered his knocking. Then a pale-faced man dressed in black came to let him in.

He was led through many dark rooms to the office of Father Pirard, whose title was Rector of the seminary.

'You're very late,' said a voice from the other end of the room.

Julien looked into the shadows, where a dark figure was seated at a desk. He felt sick with anxiety, but stepped forward to give his name.

'You have been recommended to me by Father Chélan,' said the man at the desk, 'my friend for thirty years.'

'Ah! So it is M. Pirard to whom I have the honour of talking,' said Julien in the very faintest voice.

'Obviously,' the Rector replied, looking at him crossly. Then he unfolded the letter he had received from Father Chélan and read it aloud. ' "Julien is not lacking in memory or intelligence, and he is thoughtful," says this letter. "But how strong is his faith? Is he really sincere?" Sincere!' the Rector repeated, looking astonished.

He gestured to Julien to sit on a chair beside his desk, and asked him if he could speak Latin. The young man was not too frightened to answer in perfect Latin. So a long conversation began between them. It lasted three hours, and by the end Father Pirard thought he could see why his friend had recommended this young man. He was rather impressed.

'Put Julien Sorel in cell 103,' said the Rector to the man who had brought him in. As a special favour, he was allowing Julien his own cell. But when they reached cell 103, it was a tiny little room on the top floor of the building. One small window looked out over the castle walls and the fields surrounding the town.

Julien sat down on the single wooden chair in his cell – and fell asleep. He did not hear the bell for supper or for church in the evening. When the sun came up next morning, he found himself lying on the floor.

Breakfast was Julien's first chance to meet his fellow students. There were over three hundred of them – and it was immediately obvious to Julien that almost all of them were peasants' sons. They preferred to earn their bread by singing a few words of Latin instead of labouring all day in the fields.

'Never mind,' he thought. 'Under Napoleon I'd have been an officer; among these fellows, I'll be a bishop.'

He did not realize – and he had to learn this rather painfully – that none of his fellow pupils saw any value at all in books or literature or a knowledge of the history of the Church. Any attempt by anyone to do well at his studies was regarded with deep suspicion by the whole seminary. When Julien began his studies there, he soon saw that he was very different from all the others. They just pretended to be interested in the holy life of the Church and in debating questions of philosophy. In reality, their only concerns were an easy life and the opportunities that might exist in future to make money out of being priests.

They, too, quickly saw that Julien was different. They called him Martin Luther, to make fun of his cleverness and his fondness for elegant arguments in the classroom. This led to open abuse and even threats of violence. Julien began to carry around a sharp little knife from the kitchens, and to indicate by his gestures that he would make use of it if necessary.

◆

As the weeks passed, Julien felt that he had never before been so miserable and so lonely. He thought often of Mme de Rênal, but had no news of her. It seemed that the whole world had forgotten him. In fact, Father Pirard had received a number of letters addressed to Julien, which he had read and immediately destroyed. It was clear they came from a woman who loved the young man passionately. The Rector was relieved when a letter arrived from this lady wishing Julien a last goodbye.

One day, just as it seemed that Julien's unhappiness would make him seriously unwell, he returned to his cell and found Fouqué standing by the door. The two embraced with great emotion: Julien had never been more pleased to see his old friend. He asked for all the news from home – but was not prepared for what Fouqué had to report.

'Have you not heard?' said Fouqué. 'Your pupils' mother has become extremely religious since your departure. It's said she goes off for days to pray in distant churches – even to places as far away as Dijon or Besançon.'

31

'She comes here to Besançon?' cried Julien, turning very red in the face.

'Oh yes, very often,' replied Fouqué in some surprise.

Then his friend quickly began to ask him about other things, and there was no more talk of Mme de Rênal. After Fouqué had gone, though, Julien could think of little else for days.

♦

After several months of this unhappy life, Julien had begun to develop a second personality. He was learning how to hide all his real feelings. Above all, he was learning how to avoid giving the impression that he was a person willing and able to think for himself. But there was one teacher, apart from Father Pirard himself, whom Julien trusted and enjoyed talking to with honesty, a Father Chas-Bernard.

Late one evening, Father Pirard sent for Julien. He said that Father Chas-Bernard had specially requested Julien's help preparing the cathedral of Besançon for a great religious festival that was taking place the next Sunday.

When Sunday arrived, Julien rose at five-thirty in the morning and – in his first visit to the town since arriving at the seminary – walked with Father Chas-Bernard to the cathedral. There was much work to do, decorating all the windows and laying out carpets of cloth along the floor for the procession.

Julien worked hard for several hours. Then he sat back in the cool of the cathedral to rest and enjoy the silence of the place. After a few moments he was disturbed by the sight of two very well-dressed women, who were kneeling down to pray a short distance away from him. He walked over in their direction, to see them a little better.

The sound of his footsteps made them turn their heads slightly. Suddenly one of them gave a loud cry and fainted. She fell back and was caught by her companion. Julien jumped forwards to help them, or both would have fallen awkwardly to the ground. But as he stretched out his arm, he saw who had cried out – Mme de Rênal! The other woman was her cousin, Mme Derville, who recognized Julien immediately.

'Go away, sir, go away!' said Mme Derville in the sharpest tones of anger. 'Remove yourself, if you have any decency left!'

She spoke with such authority that Julien turned away and left them without speaking. Father Chas-Bernard found him at the door of the cathedral, looking extremely pale and almost unable to walk. Thinking that Julien was ill, he sent him back to the seminary to rest.

This event shook Julien badly. He had really not recovered from it when, one morning, Father Pirard sent for him and delivered another surprise – this time, of a slightly more welcome kind. Father Pirard declared himself well pleased with Julien's progress at his studies and announced that he was promoting him: he would now be an assistant tutor.

It was a welcome development for Julien. Apart from anything else, it meant that he could at last enjoy his meals alone. He did not have to sit through any more endless stupid conversations. In fact, though, the promotion changed his life in rather deeper ways. To his great surprise, the other students began to change their behaviour towards him. They stopped calling him Martin Luther. They even began to show him some respect. By the time of the first important examinations of their year, it was generally assumed that Julien would be top of the class – and he was no longer abused for it.

Then a strange thing happened. On the day of the exams, each pupil was required to answer questions in open conversation with the visiting examiners. Julien sat down with them, and spoke brilliantly as predicted. But after ten minutes or so, the examiners suddenly began to ask rather odd questions. They wanted to know Julien's views on all sorts of issues that were known to be the subject of bitter political argument among senior members of the clergy.

Julien walked straight into their trap. Invited to speak freely, he talked with great enthusiasm – but said all the wrong things. They smiled back at him for thirty minutes. Then their smiles disappeared and Julien was rudely criticized for his views. When the exam results were announced, Julien came 193rd in the order.

How can we explain properly to the reader what had happened? The details of the trap hardly matter: to grasp all those, you would need to understand how much more the senior members of the Church of France were concerned with politics, money and influence than with spiritual matters. Like any huge political movement, the Church had its rival groups and competing interests. And this was the real point. The chief of Julien's examiners, a M. de Frilair, was a bitter enemy of Father Pirard. Julien was clearly Father Pirard's star pupil. So M. de Frilair had been determined to fail him.

Actually, something else was happening, too. Father Pirard's enemy, M. de Frilair, had been engaged for several years in a fierce legal battle over the ownership of a large piece of land near Besançon. On the other side in this battle was a certain Marquis* de la Mole, the head of one of the great aristocratic families of France. Naturally this Marquis lived in Paris – and he therefore had to leave much of the day-to-day management of his affairs in Besançon to someone who lived there. Readers who have followed this long explanation will not be surprised to learn the name of the Marquis's local agent. It was, of course, Father Pirard.

In short, M. de Frilair had plenty of reasons to want to see Father Pirard forced out of his job. He had spent many years

---

* Marquis: the title given to the head of a family placed at a high level in the French aristocracy.

trying to destroy his rival's reputation – and the scandal over Julien's examination result finally broke Father Pirard's will to resist. He wrote to the Marquis in Paris explaining everything that had happened, and resigned from his post.

The Marquis was not surprised at the news. He urged his old friend to start a new life in Paris – and he sent a generous gift of five hundred francs in a letter to Father Pirard's star pupil, mysteriously signed 'Paul Sorel'. It was intended to stop Julien feeling too discouraged by the examination results. Julien, though, decided that it had come from Mme de Rênal. Just like her, he thought, to be so kind! (Though it puzzled him that she had written not a single friendly word.)

By now the Rector felt very affectionate towards Julien. Realizing that it was time for him to leave, Father Pirard asked Julien to meet him in his study. There the two men, almost like father and son, talked together for some hours about life in the Church and the ways of the clergy. Father Pirard told Julien all about his wealthy protector. He would now go to Paris, he said, where the Marquis de la Mole would find him a secure position.

Julien grabbed his chance. If a job could be found for him, he said, he would join Father Pirard and move to Paris himself! Surely this could be arranged? True, an open invitation to Paris would be opposed by the seminary, which would do everything to stop him leaving. But Julien left his friend and protector in no doubt: he was determined to find a way out. Eventually, Father Pirard smiled and agreed to send Julien a secret message from Paris if he could help.

♦

The message arrived less than two weeks later. It was a simple, unsigned letter from near Paris that contained no clear meaning, and meant nothing to the seminary teachers. But there was a large spill of ink on the thirteenth word of the letter, and this was

the sign that Julien and Father Pirard had agreed between them.
If Julien could get to Paris, Father Pirard had found a job for him
there. Julien did not hesitate: he slipped out of the seminary the
next morning.

Before starting for Paris, though, he set off in another
direction. It was fourteen months since he had spoken with Mme
de Rênal. Does anyone suppose that he could have started a new
life in Paris without seeing her again?

Chapter 6   A Story of Two Nights

Once again, Julien went first to Fouqué's house, and spent the
night there. His friend urged, as ever, that they should become
partners together in the timber trade. Why run off to Paris, said
Fouqué, just to end up in a government job, where everyone
would blame him for things going wrong? Julien laughed at his
friend's modest ambitions – or what were considered ambitions
in the provinces, anyway. His own head was already full of the
world that lay ahead of him in Paris: the world of great events
and clever men, all scheming to get ahead and make their mark.

Julien started walking again soon after dawn the next
morning, and arrived in Verrières towards midday. His first stop
was at the house of Father Chélan – but he got a frosty welcome.
'You'll have lunch with me, then you'll leave this town without
seeing a single person,' said the old priest. A hired horse was
fetched for Julien to use.

'To hear is to obey,' replied Julien, and they talked of books
and bible studies all through the meal. Afterwards he got on the
horse and rode away.

Five kilometres from Verrières, however, Julien turned off into
a small wood and sent the horse home. He saw a peasant's house
close to the wood, with a ladder against its roof. When darkness

36

had fallen, Julien went over to the house, bought the ladder and persuaded the peasant to help him carry it down into Verrières.

They stopped below the famous walls of M. de Rênal's garden, where the peasant hurried off into the night. Julien watched him go. Then he climbed up the ladder to the top of the wall. How, he wondered, would he manage to deal with the three huge dogs that always used to guard the de Rênal household?

They barked and came rushing down towards him; but he whistled softly and the dogs crept up to let him stroke their ears. That was a good start. What kind of reception, though, could he expect from the lady of the household? Julien thought again of the letter from Paris with the five hundred francs. It gave him fresh courage, as he struggled across the dark gardens with his ladder. At last he found the path below her bedroom and stood staring up in silence.

With a trembling heart, Julien grabbed a few small stones from the path and threw them up against the shutters of her window. No reply. He leant his ladder up against the wall, climbed to the shutters and knocked on them with his hand, at first softly and then more loudly. It occurred to him that, even on a dark night like this, it would still be easy for someone to shoot at a man balancing on a ladder. He had to be bold now and force a way inside! Remembering how the shutters always used to work, he pulled at the bottom of one of them – and to his huge relief it swung open. He put his head to the window and said two or three times in a low voice: 'It's a friend.'

Still no sound came from inside, and he could see no sign of a lamp. Julien paused for a moment, then he tapped on the window with his finger. No answer. He knocked more loudly.

'Even if I have to break the glass,' he thought, 'I must put an end to this.'

While he was knocking very loudly, he thought he saw a white shadow move through the darkness of the room. At last –

there was no doubt about it – he saw the shadow moving extremely slowly towards him.

Suddenly he saw a face, pressed against the inside of the window. It was so dark that he still could not be sure it was her. Then the windows were pulled back, and Julien jumped down into the room. The white ghost moved away from him; he caught hold of its arms; it was a woman. A faint cry told him it was Mme de Rênal, and he embraced her tightly in his arms.

'Wicked man! What are you doing?' she cried. She could hardly speak for the strength of her emotions. 'Get out of this room at once and leave me!'

'After fourteen miserable months, I cannot leave without talking to you,' said Julien calmly. 'I want to know everything you've been doing while I've been away. As I have loved you, surely you cannot deny me that!'

Julien spoke with such authority that Mme de Rênal lost her courage. She stood watching stiffly as he pulled the ladder up through the window and laid it on the floor. But when she spoke again, her voice was cold and distant. It seemed to Julien that his boldness had all been for nothing, and the emotions of the moment were too much for him. He sat on the bed and wept quietly for a long time. Then he asked Mme de Rênal again for news of her year alone. She slowly began to describe it, though still in a formal tone that warned him away.

And so they began to talk. Julien heard of her letters to him; she heard how they had never arrived. They remembered together the day they had met in the cathedral at Besançon. Little by little, Julien told Mme de Rênal the whole story of his time at the seminary, until his receipt of the five hundred francs from 'Paul Sorel'.

'I never sent it!' said Mme de Rênal, and the two of them shared a moment of genuine surprise.

This began a discussion about the origin of the letter – and as they spoke, the whole situation between them changed. Julien sensed it in the dark, and knew he was safe. In fact, he could not stop himself making a quick mental analysis of the best way to make sure of his success. Though he was sitting next to a woman he truly loved, he unfortunately began to plot his moves as though he was defending himself against some cruel joke by the roughest of the students in the seminary. When he realized that Mme de Rênal was beginning to cry quietly on the bed, he knew it was time to play his last card.

'I have said goodbye to the Bishop,' said Julien. 'And now I am going to leave behind this place where I'm forgotten even by the person I've loved most in all the world. I am going to live in Paris . . .'

'Going to Paris!' cried Mme de Rênal rather loudly.

Julien could hear the despair in her voice. He stood up and took a few steps towards the window. Mme de Rênal could hold herself back no longer. She threw herself at Julien and fell into his arms.

So, after three hours of conversation, Julien won what he had passionately desired in the first two hours. It came a little late to be truthfully described as a moment of perfect happiness for him; too much hard work had gone into it. But it was a delicious moment, nevertheless.

Dawn was approaching: through the window, the shape of the trees on the mountains east of Verrières could just be seen. Julien insisted that Mme de Rênal should light her bedroom lamp. She hesitated, then did as he asked.

'Why not? We're together again, and there's nothing more I can do! But if my husband hears us, he will throw me out of the house like the miserable sinner that I am!'

'You sound just like Father Chélan!' said Julien. 'You would never have spoken like that before I went to the seminary. You really loved me then!'

From the moment he said this, Mme de Rênal appeared to forget completely all the risks that she was taking. She abandoned herself to her love of Julien. They agreed that he would hide in her room for the day, so they could spend one more night together.

It was a terrible risk. All day long it seemed that someone would discover what was happening. Even before breakfast there was a scare for them both: they had carried the ladder into the hall outside the bedroom, but a servant moved it away before they could hide it themselves. Two hours later, another of the servants was surprised to meet Mme de Rênal leaving the kitchens with a bundle of oranges and biscuits under her arm. Worst of all, M. de Rênal stayed in the house most of the day, so his wife hardly had a chance to visit her prisoner at all.

Evening arrived at last. M. de Rênal went off to play cards with his friends, and Mme de Rênal explained to the servants that she had a headache and would therefore have dinner alone in her bedroom. She rushed off to her room, with her pockets full of bread.

Julien decided when he saw her that he had never loved her more.

'Even in Paris,' he thought, 'I surely will never meet anyone with a kinder, nobler nature.'

Soon the two lovers were sitting together on the sofa in her room, laughing and whispering together about the events of the day. Then came a violent bang on the door. It was M. de Rênal.

'Why have you locked yourself in?' he called out loudly to his wife.

Julien only just had time to hide behind the sofa before she let him in. M. de Rênal was so surprised to find her fully dressed that he failed to notice Julien's hat, sitting on the floor by the sofa. Instead, he talked for an hour about how well he had played his cards that evening.

Eventually he left the room – but not for long. Julien and

Mme de Rênal had hardly begun to relax, when there was once again a loud bang on the door.

'Open the door immediately and let me in,' shouted M. de Rênal. 'There are burglars in the house. The servants found their ladder this morning!'

'This is the end of everything,' cried Mme de Rênal. 'He doesn't really believe there are burglars at all. He's going to kill us both! Well, I will happily die with you here!'

But this was not at all what Julien wished for. 'You must remember your children,' he said. 'I shall jump down from the window and get away through the garden. You throw my clothes down before your husband gets into the room. And be sure not to confess anything at all about my visit!'

Then he climbed out of the window and dropped into the darkness.

A moment later his clothes dropped beside him, and he could hear the sound of M. de Rênal's angry voice in the room. Julien grabbed his things and ran quickly down towards the wall that he had climbed the night before. He heard the whistle of a bullet as a gun was fired. The family's dogs were running silently beside him now, and a second shot apparently broke one of the dogs' legs: it began to utter terrible cries. Julien reached the edge of the gardens and leapt on to the walls, searching in the moonlight for a safe place to drop down to the road. Then he put on his clothes and ran.

An hour later he was five kilometres from Verrières, on the road to Geneva. He thought it was more likely that anyone pursuing him would search the Paris road. But it was also a lucky choice: he soon arrived at an inn where the Geneva-to-Paris mail coach was due in less than an hour.

He took the last free seat and squeezed himself into the little space that remained in the coach, for the long journey to the capital. His new life in Paris was just beginning.

Chapter 7   The Age of Boredom

Julien spent his first two days in the city just staring at the streets and the buildings all around him. There is no need to give the reader a detailed account of how he was affected by all the sights, especially those that celebrated his hero Napoleon. He enjoyed easy conversations about Napoleon with several strangers, too. One of them even offered to guide Julien around the city and spoke as warmly to him as to an old friend. But when the fellow had said goodbye, almost with tears in his eyes, Julien found that he had said goodbye to his watch as well.

On the evening of the third day he called on Father Pirard. In a cold tone of voice the old priest explained to him the kind of life that he could expect in the house of the Marquis de la Mole. Julien learned how he would wear a black suit of clothes at all times, and be employed by the Marquis as his secretary. Every day it would be his duty to reply to all the letters received at the house, following instructions written in pencil on the letters by the Marquis.

'It will be your business to make yourself useful,' said Father Pirard. 'If I were in your place, I would say very little. Above all, never talk of anything of which you know nothing. If the Marquis learns to trust you, you may earn a good salary and enjoy considerable influence. If he does not, you will return to the seminary at Besançon.'

Then Father Pirard told Julien a little about the family of the Marquis. He had a daughter and a son of nineteen, Count Norbert, who was an officer in the army. Julien smiled at this and nodded approvingly – which, however, brought a sharp look to Father Pirard's eye.

'I won't hide from you that this young man will certainly treat you as a very inferior person,' he warned Julien. 'He belongs to the aristocracy. He is also related to someone who had the honour of being guillotined in 1574 for his part in a plot against the King. You are the son of a carpenter of Verrières, and you work for his father. Be very careful how you behave.'

Julien was surprised and quite upset by the bitter tone of Father Pirard's voice. In fact, the old man simply felt that he should prepare Julien for a hard lesson in the realities of Parisian society.

'You will also,' he added in the same tone, 'see the Marquise* de la Mole. She is a tall and elegant woman, extremely polite and even more extremely insignificant. She is a very typical great lady of her class. She believes that any superior kind of person must be related to someone who won fame and honour on a battlefield before 1300. Money comes only a long way behind. Does that surprise you? We are no longer in the provinces, my friend!'

After much more of the same, Father Pirard at last stood up and gestured to Julien to follow him outside. There a coach was waiting, and very soon they arrived in front of a huge house with an enormous door. This was the Hôtel de la Mole, and Julien stood before it open-mouthed.

'Do try to look sensible,' said Father Pirard, as they were shown in by a servant. 'And watch out for the servants, who will all be trying to trick you into stupid social errors.'

After all this, it was almost a relief for Julien that his first meeting with the Marquis lasted hardly three minutes. The Marquis, a thin, elderly man who seemed rather poorly dressed, spoke briefly to his two visitors and sent them off with a quiet word to Father Pirard. This meeting, though, was the beginning of an extraordinary few weeks for Julien.

He was given new clothes to wear – all black, but much more elegant than anything he had worn at the seminary – and a small room of his own in the Hôtel de la Mole. He adjusted in no time

* Marquise: the wife of a Marquis.

at all to his life as a secretary, arriving early each day at his own desk in the splendidly decorated family library and working all morning on the Marquis's letters. The work was not difficult – but adjusting to the life of the aristocracy was a different matter entirely.

Each day Julien broke one or another little rule of the household, much to the delight of all the servants, who found his awkward manner hugely entertaining. Count Norbert, the Marquis's son, invited him to go horse-riding at the end of the first week. Not only did Julien fall off his horse on the way home, but he even admitted the accident during conversation at the dining table that evening. His openness surprised everyone who was listening.

In particular, it seemed to amuse Count Norbert's sister, Mlle Mathilde de la Mole. After laughing aloud, though, she questioned her brother closely about the whole incident. Previously, Julien had only seen her sitting silently at the table, as on earlier evenings. She was certainly very beautiful, with long golden hair and a lovely figure. But she had seemed terribly distant and severe. Suddenly now she looked quite interested and Julien dared to answer her questions himself, though none had been addressed to him directly. This was definitely not the sort of behaviour expected from someone in his position. Mathilde was impressed.

In fact, the evening dinner presented a special problem for Julien in these first weeks: he had never seen people eating in such luxury, and the rules of polite society seemed especially difficult at the table. The Marquise suggested to her husband that Julien should be sent off on a little evening job whenever they had guests to dinner; but the Marquis, impressed by Julien's progress, refused to consider it. So Julien quickly began to meet all their regular guests – of whom there were many.

And each evening after dinner he accompanied them all to the drawing room, where ice-creams and tea were served every fifteen minutes until midnight. At the end of the evening came supper and expensive wines; and this was the only reason that Julien ever stayed more than ten minutes in the room. The talk was extremely boring.

Readers unfamiliar with the ways of the aristocracy may find this surprising, but it is true. This was the Age of Boredom. The rules of the drawing room meant that under no circumstances could anyone ever mention the subject of politics, or any other matter likely to require serious opinions. An idea with any life in it at all was considered rudely out of place. In spite of good form, perfect manners, and an anxiety to please, boredom was written on every face.

None of the visitors to the Hôtel de la Mole could really be considered genuine friends of the Marquis and his wife. Both of them had a reputation for trying to escape their own boring company by wounding the feelings of other people around them: not a good way to win friends. Most of their middle-aged and elderly guests were there simply to be seen, and to be able to say that the well-connected Marquis was their friend. None of them ever said anything significant.

And nothing could be expected, either, of the few young people who called at the house to pay their respects to the Marquis. They were afraid of saying anything that might suggest they had a thought of their own, or might have read forbidden books, so they too soon fell into silence after a polite remark or two about the weather.

One morning, Julien met Father Pirard in the library: he was there to work for an hour or two on the never-ending legal battle between the Marquis and M. de Frilair.

'Sir,' said Julien suddenly, 'do you think it is part of my duties to spend every evening with the family, or are they just being kind?'

'It's a very great honour!' replied Father Pirard, deeply shocked. 'Plenty of people in Paris have tried for years to get an invitation, without success!'

'For me, sir, it's the most painful part of my job,' said Julien. 'I found it less boring in the seminary. I see even Mlle de la Mole yawning from time to time. I'm frightened I'll fall asleep in the drawing room! Couldn't you please get me permission, just occasionally, to go out and eat alone at an inn?'

Before Father Pirard could reply, a slight noise behind them made the two men turn round – and there stood Mathilde, quietly listening. She had come looking for a book, and had heard every word between them.

'There's a man,' she thought, 'with a mind of his own!'

That evening at dinner, Julien was astonished to hear Mathilde complaining to her family about how boring their drawing room had become. Then she turned to Julien and asked if he would like to join her and her younger friends, who met together each evening in a special corner of the drawing room. Julien had seen them there – with the beautiful Mathilde always at the centre of the group, sitting like a princess on a big blue sofa and surrounded by the Count of this and the young Marquis of that, together with various army officer friends of Count Norbert.

Julien gladly accepted her invitation, and certainly the evenings were now more interesting. Mathilde and her friends spent most of their time being rude about her parents' guests; they clearly considered most of them to be ridiculous in one way or another. Their private jokes and insults opened up a new world to Julien; he was often rather shocked at what he heard. Of course he seldom, if ever, spoke himself. It was almost as though these friends of Mathilde were speaking in a foreign language.

Though Julien could only listen and learn, his dark good looks did not go unnoticed. The Marquise and her daughter left Paris shortly afterwards to spend their summer in Provence, but

Mathilde thought quite often about this strange young man her father had employed.

Chapter 8   Patience Is Rewarded

Wealthy men with a keen appetite for life generally seek in business to entertain themselves rather than chase the best financial results. The Marquis de la Mole was just such a man. He bought and sold property and land, often quite successfully; but he easily lost his temper. He was always giving millions away, then getting into silly legal battles over tiny amounts. He badly needed a chief of staff to organize all his affairs and keep them running smoothly.

In this role Julien now began to do very well. He worked hard, knew his place in the household and showed great intelligence. The Marquis was soon relying on him to a remarkable extent. The understanding between them grew over the months to become more than just a business relationship. This eventually expressed itself in a most peculiar way.

Out walking in the city one day, Julien was caught in a sudden and very heavy rainstorm. Taking shelter in a café, he found himself being stared at – and by a man who reminded Julien of the waitress's lover in the café at Besançon, all those months ago. To be brief, a quarrel began and Julien challenged the man to a duel. This was foolish enough. Even sillier, though, was the fact that Julien was deceived into thinking his opponent was a nobleman called the Chevalier* de Beauvoisis. In fact, he was just a humble servant of the Chevalier, and the duel was avoided – but only just.

By the time the misunderstanding had been sorted out, though, Julien and the Chevalier had become good friends.

* Chevalier: a junior title in the French aristocracy.

47

Through the Chevalier, Julien acquired a small circle of companions among the aristocracy. Inevitably they soon discovered that he was no aristocrat, but a secretary working for the Marquis de la Mole on a salary. Wishing to see Julien, but wanting to avoid any embarrassment, the Chevalier invented the story that he was actually a natural son of one of the Marquis's many close friends in the provinces, born as the result of a scandalous love affair.

When the Marquis himself heard of this story, he liked the idea so much that he decided to adopt it himself. In this way, Julien could respectably be given a more noble position in the de la Mole household. The Marquis presented Julien with a blue coat, cut to match his usual black one. Whenever Julien wore the blue coat, said the Marquis, he would be treated as though he were a natural son of the family; and when he returned to the black coat, he could return to his duties as secretary.

◆

With this new arrangement, Julien and the Marquis became closer with every month that passed. Nobody since the death of the old army doctor in Verrières had ever spoken as kindly to Julien as the Marquis. To show the trust between them, the Marquis one day requested Julien to travel to London on his behalf and to spend two months in England completing various business matters.

We will not describe the feeling of horror, and almost of hatred, with which Julien set foot on English soil. His mad enthusiasm for Napoleon is well known to the reader. In every army or navy officer that he met, Julien saw one of Napoleon's enemies, perhaps even one of those who had locked him away for ever. But he did meet many Englishmen of noble birth. An elderly Russian aristocrat called Prince Korasoff took him around the great houses of London, where Julien was well received.

'My dear Sorel,' people said to him, 'you are a natural English lord. You have exactly that coldness and distance that we ourselves try so hard to acquire!'

When he returned to Paris, the Marquis de la Mole asked him: 'What amusing ideas have you brought me from England?' Julien remained silent. 'Well, what ideas have you brought, amusing or not?' the Marquis went on sharply.

'First of all,' said Julien, 'even the most sane Englishman is mad for one hour in the day. Secondly, all intelligence and talent lose 25 per cent of their value when you land in England. Thirdly, nothing is so beautiful, so marvellous and so appealing as an English landscape.'

'That's not bad,' said the Marquis, laughing.

Julien told him many stories about his stay in England, until the Marquis stopped him talking and grew serious. Then he announced that Julien would now wear a star of gold on his blue coat, as though he were the son of a Marquis. Anyone coming to the house on government business, to see the Marquis in his position as minister, could deal with Julien just as well.

◆

By a curious chance, the first of these visits was made by a gentleman from Verrières – M. Valenod, newly appointed a Baron. He arrived to thank the Marquis for his title, and found himself meeting with Julien. And he had some news: he was very soon going to be made the Mayor of Verrières in place of M. de Rênal. M. Valenod said it had been discovered that M. de Rênal had been secretly involved with dangerous supporters of political revolution. Julien almost fell over laughing at this.

He tried to get some news of Mme de Rênal, but the Baron appeared to remember their old rivalry and remained completely deaf to Julien's hints. He nevertheless suggested that Julien ought to give him a personal introduction to the Marquis.

'To tell you the truth,' replied Julien, who was determined to resist this bold approach, 'I'm much too humble a person at the Hôtel de la Mole to be able to introduce anyone to the Marquis.'

And that was the end of Baron Valenod's visit: he gave Julien a cold stare and left the house.

Julien's confident manner in this interview showed clearly how much he had changed since his arrival in the capital. He now had real style, and understood the art of life in Paris. This was immediately apparent to a certain person who now returned to the Hôtel de la Mole after a long time away: the Marquis's nineteen-year-old daughter, Mathilde. Nothing of the village boy remained, she saw, in either his manner or his dress. It was a very satisfactory development.

The day after her return, an invitation arrived for the whole family to attend a grand dance as guests of the Marquis de Retz. Such a sudden return to the formal routines of high society did not please Mathilde at all: she felt herself yawning at the thought of it.

'And I'm only nineteen!' she thought. 'Why should I have to suffer so many boring evenings, with such predictable companions?' Her lovely eyes looked all around her – and rested on Julien. 'At least,' she said to herself, 'this young man is not like all the rest . . .'

'M. Sorel,' she said to him in that sharp kind of voice so often affected by women of the highest class. 'M. Sorel, are you coming to M. de Retz's dance tonight?'

Julien tried to explain that he had received no invitation, but she would not listen.

'He has asked my brother to bring you, so that is decided. You must accompany Count Norbert to the ball.'

'How I dislike that great, tall girl,' thought Julien as he watched her walking away. 'Who does she think she is?' But of course he had little choice; he had to do as she had said.

It was an eventful evening.

Mathilde, as usual, was surrounded by eager admirers. Julien, amazed at the wealth on show at the Hôtel de Retz, spent some time watching her from a distance across the crowded floor.

'You must agree, she's the queen of the ball,' remarked a young man with a moustache, whose shoulder was digging into Julien's chest. It was the first of many such comments that he heard all around him, from groups of young men with moustaches. Mathilde, though, ignored them all and made her way through the crowds to talk to Julien.

'You, sir,' she said, 'you've been here for a long time. Now isn't it true that this dance is the prettiest of the season?'

The crowd turned round to see who the lucky man was from whom she seemed determined to get an answer.

'I'd hardly be a good judge of that, Mlle. My life is all spent at the writing desk. This is the first dance of its kind that I have ever seen.'

The young men with moustaches were scandalized.

Mathilde, though, was delighted. 'You're a wise man, M. Sorel,' she said, and began to ask him about the books he read and the things he liked to write.

Julien answered her politely but very coolly – then moved away with a respectful but rather cross look on his face and disappeared into the crowd. Immediately she was surrounded again by the Moustaches, and became involved in more silly, empty talk. One young aristocrat after another fought to keep her attention, while all the time her eye wandered this way and that for any sign of Julien's return.

An hour later there was still no sign of him. Mathilde moved from one room to another, until at last she heard his voice just around a corner. Julien was talking to someone about politics and about the causes of revolution – and he was talking with a real passion that she had never heard before. It almost frightened her

51

to hear him speaking so hotly; but it thrilled her, too. There was no doubt about it: to use a coarse expression, Mathilde was gripped.

The reader will understand that, like so many other rich young girls accustomed to having everything they want, Mathilde had always to be scheming for the one forbidden fruit. Worse still, she was dangerously fond of passion for its own sake. Only a real drama in her life could be relied on, or so she believed, to save her from being bored to death by polite society. So to find herself falling in love with a young man employed by her father, and of no known family background, was just ideal.

◆

The more Julien kept his distance, in the days and weeks following the dance, the more Mathilde was attracted to him. At first he had no trouble resisting her obvious attempts to flirt with him in the evenings. He found her shallow and artificial, just like all the other ladies he had met in Paris society. How very different from them Mme de Rênal had been! He often thought of her now, and missed her terribly. Her charm! Her simple ways! Julien felt a fool to have left her behind so easily. He deeply regretted that all his ideas about life in Paris had stopped him appreciating the true worth of a genuinely superior person.

Then, one evening, Mathilde arrived at the family dinner all dressed in black from head to toe. Julien was amazed to see her behaving as if a close relative had died. Only later could he find someone to tell him what it was all about. Apparently, Mathilde was overcome with grief on this same day every year. It marked the date on which, in the year 1574, a certain Boniface de la Mole had had his head cut off for his part in a famous plot against the King of France.

What really excited the girl about this bit of family history, though, was the fact that Boniface had been the Queen of

France's secret lover. And Mathilde loved every detail of the story. The Queen had suffered enormously in the hours before Boniface was executed. Afterwards she had boldly asked for her lover's head to be sent to her, and she had taken this head with her in her carriage at midnight and buried it with her own hands on a hillside outside Paris. Mathilde could not possibly imagine anything more romantic!

When he heard all this, Julien was impressed. Here, after all, was someone with at least some sense of history. It certainly made Mathilde seem a lot more interesting. So the next time she approached him to talk in private, Julien did not hurry to get away. He exchanged ideas with her about French history and literature, and was surprised to discover how much she knew.

Time passed, and their evening conversations grew more and more personal. Julien even revealed to her his passion for Napoleon, which shocked her but seemed to make no difference at all to her attitude towards him. Suddenly Julien grasped the truth.

'Either I'm mad,' he thought to himself, 'or she's in love with me.'

How should he react? Julien considered his options carefully for some days. Then he made up his mind, with a fierce look in his eye.

'I'll get her,' he said half aloud to himself, 'and make her love me for ever – and bad luck to any man who stands in my way . . .'

Chapter 9   Lessons in Love

Julien had much to learn. He was mistaken when he believed that a peasant's son from a small town in the provinces could easily win the heart of a Parisian society girl like Mlle de la Mole. Life is not so simple.

Watching Mathilde fall in love with him was the easy part. She made little attempt to hide her sudden passion: this affair was going to be her solution to the Age of Boredom! All the young Moustaches were amazed; some, who had invested a lot of time pursuing Mathilde as a possible wife, reacted with anger, even disgust. This did not discourage her at all.

She spent hours flirting with Julien in the library. She went regularly to the opera, knowing that Julien would be there, so that she could flirt with him in the interval. Finally, when the moment seemed exactly right, she sent a servant to Julien's room with a letter; it was purely and simply a declaration of love.

By the time he opened it, Julien was ready. He had maintained a cool appearance on most occasions; but to be chased by such a beautiful and determined girl for so long was more than he could cope with. He had begun to dream all day about her wonderful figure, her excellent taste in dress, the whiteness of her hands, the loveliness of her arms, the easy style of her movements around the drawing room. In short, he had fallen in love himself. As he read Mathilde's letter, it swept away his last defences.

'And so I,' he suddenly cried, with a passion too strong to be held back, 'I, a poor peasant, have received a declaration of love from a great lady!'

He went off into the gardens of the house and wandered around them, madly happy. It only increased his joy to think of the names of all those aristocrats in the drawing room that Mathilde had ignored when she chose him.

True, this did give him a moment or two of discomfort. At one of their daily meetings, the Marquis suddenly remarked to Julien: 'I'm very glad you're here. I like seeing you about.'

'And here am I, planning to be his daughter's lover!' thought Julien.

Possibly this could prevent Mathilde marrying the son of a famous nobleman and lifting the de la Mole family to great heights – the very thing that the Marquis hoped for, above all else. For a moment Julien thought of leaving the house and Mathilde for ever.

Almost immediately, though, it occurred to him that a noble gesture like this would be ridiculously generous. These aristocratic families had so many advantages already; why should he try to protect their best interests for them? It was each man for himself in this desert of selfishness that men call life! He, a poor peasant from Verrières, had to wear a horribly dull black coat year after year. Twenty years earlier he would have been in a scarlet uniform just like all those rich young men of the drawing room! And in those days, a man like him was either killed in battle or was a general serving Napoleon by the age of thirty-six!

'Well anyway,' said the devil inside him at last, 'I'm cleverer than all of them, when it really matters. I know how to choose the uniform of my day. Scarlet or black, it's all the same to me: I'm at war, either way!'

It must be admitted that the look in his eyes at this moment was not a pretty one: he looked almost like a common criminal. The light in the garden was fading. Drunk with a sense of his own power and happiness, Julien went off to the opera.

◆

From this point, things grew harder for Julien.

Mathilde quickly acted on her letter (and a stream of other letters in the days that followed) by challenging him to pay her a midnight visit in her bedroom. He managed to do this, though it took all his courage – mostly because Julien actually suspected he was being led into a trap set for him by Mathilde and all the Moustaches. He climbed through the window into her bedroom with his pockets stuffed full of pistols, which was not the most romantic start to the occasion.

What followed was exciting enough – they became lovers, as

both of them had intended. For Julien, though, it was nothing like his first experience with Mme de Rênal. There was none of her innocence, her tenderness. It was as though he and Mathilde were imitating a passionate love for each other, not really feeling it.

'This fine life in Paris,' thought Julien unfairly, 'can spoil everything – even love.'

But he had achieved his ambitious goal and was happy enough to have done that.

Mlle de la Mole, meanwhile, shared nothing of this slight disappointment – but for the worst possible reason. For her, the actual business of making love with Julien had really been little more than her duty, after leading him on so strongly. The cruel fact was, she had already decided by then that the excitement of the chase was fading.

Worse, she had begun to have serious second thoughts about the wisdom of a love affair with a man from the very lowest level of society.

'Can I have been mistaken?' she said to herself, after Julien had safely escaped from her bedroom. 'Can it be that I don't love him after all?'

♦

A long and painful period followed for Julien. She would treat him kindly one day, and then speak to him like a servant the next. Suddenly all their private conversations about history, politics and literature seemed to be nothing more for Mathilde than an excuse to speak about one or other of the young Moustaches and the great deeds performed by all their noble families in the history of France. She would sit with Julien in the garden and then talk quite happily for hours about all the private details of her past love affairs.

This naturally made Julien wild with jealousy. It can be seen that he had little experience of life; he had not even read any novels. If he had been a little less clumsily shy, he could have remarked coolly to this girl: 'Ah yes, but at the end of the day, I am the man you really love!' At least then he might have captured Mathilde's interest again.

Instead, he spoke out honestly. 'So you no longer love me, while I cannot live without you!' he said to her one evening, mad with love and grief.

It was almost the worst mistake he could have made. This stupid remark altered the whole situation in a moment. Mathilde, sure of being loved now, felt complete contempt for him. Within days, she was treating him like an inferior being who could be made to love her as and when she wanted.

Her treatment of Julien went from bad to worse. A clear rejection might almost have been kinder. It was the constant changes in her attitude that left him sick with anxiety. She was still capable of being the romantic lover: when Julien decided one night to risk everything with a surprise visit to her bedroom, she received him with open arms and swore she could never live without him again. Julien had never experienced such a physical passion as she displayed that night. When he left her, she even cut off a great wave of her blonde hair as a present for him to keep – which caused him some embarrassment at the dinner table next day, when he saw where the scissors had done their work.

Within a few days, however, she had rearranged her hair to cover the gap completely. She looked away at the table when he tried to catch her eye. She ignored him in the drawing room.

Finally, approaching him in the library one morning, she announced: 'If you have no sense of honour, you can ruin me. But that danger won't prevent me from being sincere. I no longer love you, sir; my crazy passion deceived me.'

And she left him standing there, too astonished to reply.

This certainly seemed to mark the end of the affair. At last Julien could now see how little he had ever really understood of

Mathilde's character. He soon found a private moment to tell her that his love for her was totally destroyed. The truth, of course, was different: he knew his emotions were still completely ruled by Mathilde – but by leaving Paris, perhaps, he would somehow be able to recover.

And it was at this moment, as if by an act of God, that the Marquis sent for Julien and announced that he had a special assignment for him. The two of them would leave Paris together immediately, to attend a secret political meeting of the greatest importance outside the city. Julien understood very little about the whole business – but it meant he could leave Paris for a time and try to forget Mathilde. This was all that mattered for the moment.

For the Marquis, meanwhile, the secret meeting was an event of the greatest importance. He needed Julien at his side because he knew the young man would be able to memorize all that he heard at the meeting. It would be Julien's important task to leave immediately afterwards and report a detailed account of the meeting to a powerful friend of the Marquis, living in a small town far away from the capital.

◆

When Julien finally found his way to the friend of the Marquis, after many curious adventures, he got quite a surprise. He delivered his report, as he had been instructed to do – and was then told to travel directly to the city of Strasbourg, and to stay there for twelve days before returning to Paris. Unable to argue, but unable to understand the reason for all his travels either, Julien arrived in Strasbourg feeling depressed and lonely.

Never since leaving Verrières, in fact, had he felt so low. Above all, the failure of his relationship with Mathilde clouded his view of everything: the young man who had once been so confident of his future now looked forward without much hope of succeeding at anything.

The night, though, is often at its darkest just before the dawn. Three days after his arrival, Julien was riding his horse through the city when a shout made him raise his head. It was Prince Korasoff, the wise old Russian with whom he had spent such a happy time in London. They were soon eating and drinking together in the best inns in Strasbourg. The Prince noticed at once the sadness of his friend, and listened kindly as Julien poured out his sorrows. Then the younger man began to receive some advice on how he could rescue the situation with Mathilde.

'All is not lost,' said the Prince. 'Here is what you must do. First, go home and show yourself to this lady as you were before your affair began. Be careful not to behave coldly or let her think you are offended. Second, make an effort to see her every day. And third, you must concentrate all your romantic efforts on another woman whom she knows well. You will have to pretend day and night, and if your game is discovered, then you are lost! But if you can continue it, I think you will find that your Mathilde is less in command of the situation than she supposes.'

Julien sincerely admired the Prince. He took his words to heart – and in more ways than one. The Prince insisted that well-written love letters would be essential to a successful conclusion, and presented his friend with copies of fifty-three letters that he himself had used for romantic assignments in Russia. Only the odd detail needed to be changed. Otherwise the sentences in them could be copied out exactly and would provide Julien with a most elegant weapon in his battle to recover Mathilde!

◆

Julien carried the letters back with him to Paris, and by the time he reached the Hôtel de la Mole he had already chosen the woman lucky enough to receive them. Her name was Mme de Fervaques, the widow of a general, and a regular visitor in the evenings.

Julien started to put the plan into action the next evening. He dressed for dinner in the simplest travelling clothes that he could find. Mathilde arrived last, always faithful to her habit of keeping people waiting. Seeing Julien, she went very red; no one had told her of his return. Dinner passed very pleasantly. The Marquis praised Julien to everyone for the task that he had just completed. Then, at eight o'clock, Mme de Fervaques arrived. Julien immediately slipped away, and shortly afterwards reappeared, dressed with the greatest possible care.

He sat next to Mme de Fervaques in the drawing room, when he was sure that Mathilde could see them together. And he made the general's widow the one and only object of all his attention until she rose to leave. She announced that she was going on to the opera. Julien hurried straight there, found a seat near her private box and stared at her throughout the performance.

All Mlle de la Mole's ideas were immediately changed at the sight of Julien.

'Really and truly,' she said to herself, 'that man is my natural husband. If I sincerely want to live my life honestly and honourably, he is obviously the man I ought to marry!'

Expecting to find Julien as miserable now as he had been before his secret work, she decided to approach him without delay and to explain exactly how she felt about him. But here was a peculiar thing: each time she made it obvious that she was available to talk with him, Julien seemed to be occupied elsewhere. And she could not help noticing that, more often than not, he was occupied with talking to Mme de Fervaques.

Faithful to the plan of behaviour suggested to him by Prince Korasoff, Julien chose a position every evening close beside Mme de Fervaques' chair. Unfortunately, he then generally found it impossible to think of a single word to say to her. She seemed to him to be made of wood. Her aristocratic manner reflected not just an extreme form of politeness, but a complete inability to feel any emotion at all. Her conversation consisted entirely of meaningless talk about the royal family, hunting and her own family history.

But the Russian's letters were very useful. Julien copied out the first of them a week later. Its contents made him laugh aloud.

'Is it possible,' he asked himself, 'that any young man exists who could honestly write this kind of stuff?'

Nevertheless, he finished the copy and delivered it just as Prince Korasoff had instructed.

♦

Julien sent fifteen letters before he received the first response from the great lady. A letter was handed to Julien in the library one morning. It was an invitation from Mme de Fervaques to visit her house for dinner.

The food was dull and the conversation might have driven a man to drink. Julien hated everything about the occasion. But it was quite clear from Mme de Fervaques' attitude towards him that progress was being made. In fact, the letters had persuaded her that this Julien Sorel was a rather remarkable young man.

The day after the dinner, Julien narrowly avoided a serious embarrassment: he sent off another copied letter and forgot to change the place names in it. Mme de Fervaques was very puzzled by references to that week's activities in *London*. But she quickly allowed Julien to talk his way out of it, and could hardly wait to receive the next letter.

When it did not arrive for a couple of days, Mme de Fervaques wrote a letter of her own and sent it off to the Hôtel de la Mole, where she assumed a servant would deliver it to Julien. The letter, addressed to M. Sorel, was lying on a table in the library when Mathilde wandered in, searching for an opportunity to talk privately with Julien.

'This is what I cannot bear,' cried Mathilde, seizing the letter and guessing where it had come from. 'You are forgetting me completely, sir! Your behaviour is shocking!'

Julien was amazed. Everything had happened just as Prince Korasoff had predicted. This proud girl was now passionately jealous of her rival! Julien kept at a distance from her for just another few days – the Prince would have been proud of him. But at last he could no longer control his passion. As he and Mathilde walked together in the garden one evening, he stopped and took her hand.

Tears flooded to his eyes as he lifted her hand to his lips and made his confession. He had been hiding his feelings, but could do so no longer. He loved her and could not live another day without a guarantee of her love for him.

Mathilde was overcome. She threw her arms around him. Within the hour, she was proposing that they should run away together to London . . .

For the first time in her life, Mathilde was genuinely in love. Life, until now, had always seemed to move too slowly. Suddenly she had never been happier – or less cautious. In the drawing room each evening, she would call Julien to her side for long private discussions watched by fifty people or more. All her conversations somehow led Mathilde back to a question or two that only Julien could answer.

◆

Then one day, Mathilde found that she was pregnant.

She was filled with joy and proudly announced the news to Julien.

'Do you doubt me now?' she asked. 'Isn't this the best possible guarantee of my love? Now I'm your wife for ever.'

For some moments Julien was so surprised that he could not find the words to reply. So many different emotions were battling inside him. He had become accustomed to treating Mathilde with as much coolness as possible – but now he wanted to embrace and protect her. He admired her courage; but he was frightened for her, too. And how could they possibly tell her father?

Mathilde herself seemed determined to inform him immediately. If the Marquis reacted badly, she said, then she and Julien would just have to leave together and start a new life elsewhere.

'But we'll go out by the front door, in the full light of day!'

This was too much for Julien. The thought of telling the Marquis filled him with horror. He was not exactly afraid. But he knew that the Marquis wanted above all to see his daughter marry into one of the other great families of France. Now it was Julien's terrible duty to announce the end of that dream. He knew how painful this would be for the Marquis. And if he was honest, there was something else that worried Julien, too: he feared that a long separation might be forced on the two of them ... and that within six months Mathilde would forget all about him.

When he confessed all these worries to her, Mathilde was secretly delighted. Here at last, she thought, was Julien confirming his love! He had played his part so well, for so long, that she had begun to feel unsure of his real emotions. Now she was confident again, and loved him even more – but still nothing would persuade her to postpone telling the Marquis her news.

So she wrote her father a long letter the next evening, with a note on the envelope instructing him to open it only when he was alone. It was handed to the Marquis at midnight, as he returned to the house from a party. He glanced at it and made his way to the library, closing the door behind him.

Chapter 10   Days of Despair

Julien sat in his bedroom, with his head in his hands. What was his duty now? And how could he possibly hope to save his career? He was just picking up his pen to try writing his thoughts down on paper when he was interrupted by the Marquis's oldest servant.

'The Marquis asks you to come at once, whether you are dressed or not.' As he walked down the stairs beside Julien, the old fellow added quietly: 'The master is mad with anger. You'd better be careful.'

Julien wondered for a moment whether the Marquis might make a physical attack on him. He did not – but for the first time in his life, perhaps, this noble lord made no attempt at all to be polite. He screamed insults at Julien that might have come from a coach-driver. His anger was uncontrollable. When Julien tried to explain his love for Mathilde, it only made things worse.

'You ought to have gone away, sir,' said the Marquis. 'It was your duty to go . . . You are the lowest of mankind . . .'

The shame and regret that Julien felt in his presence were perfectly genuine. He could see that he had done the Marquis a great wrong. Going to the table, he bent over and wrote a quick note to the Marquis. It announced his decision to kill himself.

'I am going to the garden,' said Julien, 'so you may order your servants to shoot me, and no one will ever know the truth.'

By the time he reached the garden, though, Julien had already begun to have second thoughts about this plan. Was he not going to be a father soon, after all, and did this not mean being responsible for his child? Of course nothing happened in the garden, and after ten minutes he returned to his bedroom and started packing his clothes. He left the Hôtel de la Mole soon after, and rode out into the country.

Mathilde was in despair when she read the note the next

morning, and found Julien gone. A dramatic meeting followed between her and the Marquis.

'If he's dead, then I'll die too!' cried Mathilde. 'And you'll be the cause of my death . . . Possibly you'll be glad of it . . . But if I go on living, I swear on Julien's departed soul that I'll dress in black at once and be known all over Paris as his widow, Mme Sorel. I will send out cards inviting all of society to the funeral, you may rely on it . . . You won't find me a coward!'

The poor Marquis was trapped. Between his anger at Julien and his fear of Mathilde, he changed his mind ten times a day over the best way forward. True, he was desperate to see his daughter matched with an heir of the aristocracy. But this was partly because of his own experience as a young man in the 1790s, when the revolution in France had forced him to escape from his country and face an uncertain future. This same experience perhaps also made him a little more sympathetic to Julien's situation.

◆

Julien himself spent the next few weeks staying outside Paris with Father Pirard (who was angry with him but not as surprised as Julien had expected). Mathilde rode out to see him every day. She loved him a little more truly with every meeting.

More important, she was determined now to manage things with the Marquis so that a happy result could be found for them both.

Step by step, she steadily persuaded her father to improve the terms of the deal he was prepared to offer them. First he agreed a sum of money that would at least provide the couple with a safe future. Then he promised them a large property in the south-west of France, which would allow Julien to adopt a change of name and become M. Sorel de la Vernaye. Finally, the Marquis made arrangements for Julien to be offered a position in the army – as an officer in a cavalry regiment, the Fifteenth Hussars based in Strasbourg.

Even now, though, the Marquis still had his doubts. It could not be denied that Julien was a brilliant young man, with a bold heart. But deep down in his character, the Marquis found something alarming. And since this seemed to be the impression that Julien made on everyone, there had to be some truth in it.

Above all, there was the most obvious worry. Had Julien really fallen in love with Mathilde, overcome by romantic passion? Or had he been coldly plotting from the beginning to win Mathilde's love, knowing that her father loved her more than anything else in the world, and knowing also that he had an income of several hundred thousand francs a year? That was a question that the Marquis could not answer.

So his letter to Mathilde informing her about the officer's position with the Hussars was not his last word. When Mathilde wrote back to him, thanking him for all his kindness but insisting still that she should be allowed to marry Julien at a big public wedding very soon, she got a surprise. Her father's reply was a fierce one:

Obey me, or I will withdraw my entire offer. Tremble, my proud girl. I do not yet know what sort of man your Julien is, and you know even less than I do. Let him leave for Strasbourg and be careful to behave himself. I will let you know my wishes in two weeks' time.

The letter astonished Mathilde. She could see that she had no choice, though; she had to agree to her father's decision. So that evening she told Julien of all that had been decided, and that he could now consider himself an officer in the Hussars.

He was overcome with emotion. It seemed almost too good to be true. So this peasant's son, who was always dreaming about the brave deeds of Napoleon, would now have the chance to wear his own scarlet uniform! More than that, he would be starting his army career with a family behind him and a new name as well. This, it has to be admitted, brought less noble thoughts to his mind.

'At last,' he said to himself, 'my romantic story reaches its conclusion, and in the end I have got what I wanted! I have managed to win the love of this hugely proud creature,' he thought, looking at Mathilde. 'Her father cannot live without her, and she cannot live without me!'

Next morning, a pair of horses and a coach arrived at Father Pirard's house to take Julien to join his regiment. The old priest passed on to him twenty thousand francs, a gift from the Marquis.

'He expects you to spend them within the next year, taking care, however, not to make yourself look ridiculous,' said Father Pirard. (Father Pirard himself thought such a large sum of money was just a cause of sin.) An agreement had also been made with the local authorities, he added, to have Julien recognized as a young man of noble birth.

◆

In short, Julien arrived in Strasbourg with everything he could have desired to begin his new life. And when the Fifteenth Regiment of Hussars rode out for a march three days later, many women in the streets of the city turned their heads to watch a very good-looking man as he passed them. It was Lieutenant de la Vernaye, riding near the front on the finest horse in the region, which had cost him six thousand francs.

It took only a week or so for the other officers to reach a favourable opinion of the new man. His severe look and calm, confident manner began to win him a reputation from the start. Anyone who saw him standing with his sword in his hand, and his obvious pride in every detail of the Hussars uniform, could have no doubt that here was an ambitious soldier with a great future before him.

'This young man,' said the older officers to each other, 'has everything except youth.'

Then, in the middle of riding exercises one morning, Julien was surprised to see a young servant from the Hôtel de la Mole approaching him with a letter. Julien took it and opened it immediately. His face went white as he read it.

All is lost [wrote Mathilde]. *Hurry here as quickly as possible, give up everything. If necessary leave the regiment without permission. As soon as you arrive in Paris, wait for me near the little door into our garden. I will come out to speak to you. I may perhaps be able to let you into the garden. All is lost, I fear, and for ever. Depend on me, you will find me reliable and loyal. I love you.*

Julien was very soon riding at full speed out of Strasbourg on the road to Paris. He changed to a carriage at Metz and arrived at five in the morning outside the garden door of the Hôtel de la Mole. Mathilde quickly appeared and threw herself into his arms.

'All is lost! My father has left the city. We don't know where he has gone. But here is a letter from him: read it.'

Tears streaming down her face, she got into Julien's carriage and sat beside him as he opened it and began reading.

I could forgive everything [wrote the Marquis] *except the fact that he had a deliberate plan to seduce you into marriage. I promise you that I will never agree to a marriage with that man. I will pay him to live abroad, far away from France and best of all in America. If you doubt my reasons, read this letter that I have received from his previous employer, Mme de Rênal…*

Here Julien stopped, astonished, and looked up at Mathilde.

'Where is Mme de Rênal's letter?' he asked her coldly.

'Here it is,' said Mathilde. 'I didn't want to show it to you until I had shown you my father's reaction.'

Julien read the letter:

What I owe to God and moral truth, Sir, means I have an obligation to write this note to you. It is my duty, which must come before the sense of sorrow that I feel. You have asked me about the behaviour of a certain young man. I must tell you, Sir, it was not satisfactory. Poor, grasping creature! He attempted to make a position for himself and to become somebody by seducing a weak and unhappy woman. I believe he has no religious principles at all. He has decided that to be successful as a tutor in any household, he will seduce the woman who has most influence there. Then his only goal is to win control over the master of the house and his money. [And so the text continued for several pages.]

This letter, extremely long and marked in many places by signs of tears, was certainly written by Mme de Rênal; in fact it had obviously been written with special care.

'I cannot blame your father,' said Julien when he had finished reading it. 'He is right and wise. What father would want his dear daughter to marry such a man! Good-bye!'

Julien jumped out of the carriage and in a moment was gone. Mathilde tried to follow him for a few steps down the street, but he walked so rapidly away that she could only turn and run back through the garden door.

Julien made his way back to the coaching inn and took the first available carriage in the right direction. He arrived in Verrières on a Sunday morning. The local gun shop was open and Julien stopped there to buy two pocket pistols. At his request, the shopowner loaded them.

The bells of Verrières church were just ringing to signal the start of the service. Julien entered the church. He quickly found his way to a spot just a little way behind Mme de Rênal's usual place – and there he found her, praying on her knees. The sight of this woman who had loved him so dearly made Julien's arm tremble so much that he hesitated for a moment over his plan.

'I can't do it,' he said to himself. 'I'm physically unable to do it.'

At that moment, the bells stopped and Mme de Rênal bowed her head. Julien could no longer see her face so plainly. He fired a shot at her with one pistol and missed her. He fired a second shot; she fell to the ground.

Chapter 11   A Strange Calm

Screams filled the church. There was a great rush for the doors. Julien began walking slowly towards them, but was knocked over by the crowd. As he got up again, he was seized by a police sergeant – and in no time at all found himself locked up in Verrières prison.

Mme de Rênal had not been seriously wounded. The first bullet had passed through her hat and the second through her shoulder – where it struck and broke the bone but otherwise did no damage. The doctor who attended to her thought this would be welcome news. Instead, it seemed to leave his patient deeply upset.

The truth was, Mme de Rênal would have preferred to die. She had been hoping for death ever since her priest had forced her to write that terrible letter to the Marquis de la Mole. Her grief over losing Julien had been bad enough; but her pain over the letter had finally ended her desire to live. She knew, though, that it was a crime against God to take her own life, so she had welcomed death at someone else's hand. It seemed right that that hand should be Julien's!

As soon as the doctor had left her, Mme de Rênal sent a servant off to the prison with some money for the guards, so that Julien would be treated kindly. The sergeant in charge took the money but made no effort to speak with Julien for two days. He did allow him some paper and a pen, though, with which Julien wrote a passionate letter to Mathilde. He commanded her never to think of him again and to start a new life without him immediately.

Julien was determined that he would die for his crime. 'I am guilty of deliberate murder,' he told the magistrate who visited him on his first day in the prison. 'The law is quite clear. I deserve death, and I expect it. You, sir, will have the pleasure of announcing the death sentence.'

The following day, however, the prison sergeant himself brought Julien his supper – and with it the news that Mme de Rênal was expected to make a full recovery.

'What! She's not dead?' cried Julien, astonished. He asked the sergeant several questions, to satisfy himself that he was being told the truth. Then he ordered the man out of the cell, and fell down weeping on the bed. They were hot tears of joy and thanks. If he had ever doubted it, Julien could no longer hide from himself the depth of his love for Mme de Rênal. In this moment of great emotion, he truly believed in God. What did it matter if the Church of France was rotten and run by selfish men?

It soon occurred to him that perhaps Mme de Rênal might forgive him and even love him again, if she had the chance. He started to think about the possibility of planning an escape to Switzerland. That same evening, however, a carriage arrived to take him away to Besançon. And there he was locked up in the ancient prison of the castle – hardly a couple of kilometres away from his old cell at the seminary.

Now a curious thing happened: no longer ambitious to succeed in the wider world, he felt a sudden, strange sense of calm in his mind. He looked at everything in a new way – and found himself thinking only very seldom of Mathilde. He thought about Mme de Rênal day and night. And each time he thought of her, he was overcome with relief that his shot had not been fatal.

'What a surprise!' he said to himself. 'I thought that by her letter to the Marquis de la Mole she had destroyed my future happiness for ever. But less than two weeks later, here I am giving hardly a thought to all the worries that concerned me then. And life goes on, after all! All I need are my books, and I shall be content!'

♦

While Julien himself may have been content, though, many others were not. Stories of his crime and capture were the talk of the region. Within days, his friend Fouqué arrived in Besançon to see him. He was soon asking everyone he knew for a way to help Julien.

By chance, one of Fouqué's customers was M. de Frilair, that same powerful priest who had been responsible for ending Julien's career in the seminary. M. de Frilair was extremely interested to hear from Fouqué all the details of Julien's life since those days. He began to wonder whether his own career might benefit from these events, in a way that would become clear if he was patient. M. de Frilair did not have to wait long.

Shortly after Fouqué's trip to Besançon, Julien was woken just after dawn by another visitor: his cell door was opened, and a woman dressed as a peasant threw herself into his arms. It was Mlle de la Mole.

She had heard the news by going to Verrières, she said – and it was cruel of Julien to have told her nothing helpful in his letter. But she forgave him everything. It was not a crime he had committed, but a noble act of revenge! She had come dressed as a peasant only to avoid embarrassing her father. But together they would now find a way out of the crisis.

Julien received her quite coldly at first and was cross at her refusal to obey his letter. But she declared her love for him so passionately, and was so wildly emotional about the whole situation, that Julien could hardly resist her. Somewhere in the back of his mind lay a suspicion (which he hardly even admitted to himself) about Mathilde's true motives. But he was as strongly attracted to her as ever.

So he abandoned himself to her love; there was something mad and rather grand about it that he had to admire. Mathilde herself did not hesitate for a moment. Julien was everything she had ever hoped for in a lover – more romantic, even, than her tragic Boniface de la Mole!

But how could she get him safely back to Paris? He would have to face a trial for attempted murder. Therefore something had to be done to make sure of a sympathetic jury. She went to see all the best lawyers in the region. She offended them one by one, offering them pieces of gold rather more openly than was usual. They all took the money, of course, but could not really help her.

It was soon clear to Mathilde that there was only one individual in the area really worth consulting if she wanted any kind of helpful 'arrangement' with a jury. His name was M. de Frilair.

Therefore Mathilde went to see him. Or, more accurately, she waited a whole week in Besançon for him to grant her the privilege of a meeting, and then went to see him. Mathilde had been told that he was a powerful leader of the clergy. Even so, she was surprised by the wealth that was on display in his house. Being there was just like being back in Paris!

There was a surprise for M. de Frilair, too. It took him only a few minutes to persuade Mathilde to confess that she was using a false name. He was astonished, though, to be dealing with the daughter of his old enemy, the Marquis de la Mole. He listened carefully to Mathilde's appeal for help to get Julien acquitted. And he sat up quickly in his chair when Mathilde mentioned Mme de Fervaques. She was, M. de Frilair knew, a person of great influence in the selection of bishops of France.

The effect of Mme de Fervaques' name on M. de Frilair was quite visible to Mathilde, who was confident that she had at last found a way to help Julien. M. de Frilair began to talk quite boldly about his influence in the region: it would be very unlucky indeed, he claimed, if a jury were found for the trial that did not contain at least eight or nine of his friends! Besides, the story of Julien's love affair with Mme de Rênal was known to everyone and . . .

Here M. de Frilair stopped suddenly. He could see that his words had struck Mathilde like lightning. She had known nothing, he saw, of the whole affair! She had never even guessed at it!

Now it was his turn to take control of the discussion. Cruelly, he played with Mathilde's emotions. He described in great detail everything he had heard about Julien's life in the de Rênal household. Poor Mathilde sat through it all in a state of shock. But she said nothing of her feelings to M. de Frilair, and left him only after he had assured her of his help with the jury.

♦

Mathilde was careful in her next few meetings with Julien: it was important, she could sense, not to challenge him about his past. As the days passed, though, the truth became clear to her: their relationship was not quite the romantic drama she had supposed. Julien always received her kindly, but it was in a mysterious way apparent to both of them that her visits and her talk were beginning actually to bore him.

One day, with a feeling of terror in her heart, she uttered Mme de Rênal's name. She saw Julien tremble. So it was all true! From that moment, jealousy of this unknown woman simply increased Mathilde's own passion for Julien: it was now beyond her control.

Some days later, suspecting that she knew everything, Julien decided to mention the situation openly.

'I have a favour to ask you,' he said to Mathilde. 'When our child is born, send it to be looked after by a nurse in Verrières. Mme de Rênal will watch the nurse carefully.'

'That's a very hard thing to say to me . . .' said Mathilde, turning pale. They both knew his meaning.

'That's true, and I ask your pardon a thousand times,' cried Julien, and embraced her in his arms.

But he soon came back to the same idea. He begged Mathilde to understand what he was saying. If he lost his trial and his life, then she would be able to marry again – but the child of her first marriage would always be treated in Paris as a terrible mistake.

'Forgive me, my dear,' said Julien. 'But in fifteen years' time, Mme de Rênal will love my son and you will have forgotten him.'

This was followed by a long silence between them. Then Mathilde turned and sadly left the cell.

Julien did not know, of course, how hard she was struggling in secret to make sure he did *not* lose his trial. He himself, meanwhile, did nothing at all to help his own cause. He refused to allow the lawyer for his own defence to argue that he had been temporarily mad; he treated all the meetings with the lawyers as a waste of time.

But Mathilde refused to be discouraged. She managed over the next few weeks to advance matters between Mme de Fervaques and M. de Frilair so that private letters were exchanged between them. Indeed, the magic word *bishop* was even written down.

The choice of jury members for a trial was always a delicate matter: the process involved the selection of thirty-six names, from which a final twelve could be picked. But M. de Frilair regarded the situation as 'under control' after he had looked through the list of thirty-six. One of them, he saw, was a M. Valenod – the man whom he had been responsible for getting appointed as Mayor of Verrières, and almost as reliable as a member of his own church staff.

◆

Reports about the selection of the jury were now filling every newspaper in the region – and they were examined more closely in the de Rênal household in Verrières than anywhere else. When the list of thirty-six was published, and landed on their breakfast table, Mme de Rênal looked across at her husband and announced her decision: she was going to go to Besançon.

M. de Rênal dropped the bread that he was holding and stared back in horror.

'Please understand my position,' begged the former Mayor of Verrières. 'That fellow Valenod will unite with M. de Frilair and they will do everything they can to make things unpleasant for me!'

Mme de Rênal then had to sit through a long lecture about public morals. Of course this made no difference. She simply promised her husband that she would avoid any kind of personal publicity, then made her plans and set off for Besançon.

As soon as she arrived there, she wrote in person to each of the names on the list of thirty-six.

I shall not appear on the day of the trial [she wrote] *in case it harms M. Sorel's position. I desire only one thing in the world, and I desire it passionately – that he should be acquitted.*

Julien, she explained, had always been the victim of occasional fits of madness. But he was nevertheless a very extraordinary person, as everyone who knew him in Vergy and Verrières would agree. The idea that he might be sent to the guillotine for his silly attack on her was too horrible to consider. If they even thought for a moment of spilling the blood of an innocent man, then she would throw herself at their feet to defend him . . .

Naturally, news of the letter spread quickly round the town. Public interest in the crime increased again: it seemed the most exciting thing to have happened in Besançon for years. A single day had been fixed for Julien's trial: finding a vacant hotel room in the town around that day was already impossible. Pictures of

Julien were being sold in every inn. Every woman in Besançon was desperate to have the promise of a seat in the courtroom.

♦

Finally the day arrived. Mme de Rênal prayed that her appeal to the jury would succeed. Mathilde showed M. de Frilair a letter that she had obtained from the most senior bishop in France, requesting that Julien should be acquitted. (M. de Frilair assured her that everything possible had been done. They could rely on M. Valenod, he said, to frighten the stupid members of the jury into reaching the right decision.) But no one really knew what would happen – and this only added to all the excitement.

When the police sergeants arrived at the courtroom with Julien, just after nine in the morning, they had difficulty fighting their way in through all the crowds. Taking up his position opposite the jury, Julien looked around him. He was amazed (and very pleased) to see a dozen or so extremely pretty women sitting quite close to him.

In fact, there were beautiful women all around the room – and the arrival of Julien, looking pale but nevertheless extremely good-looking and not a day over twenty years old, caused a sudden pause in all their talking. For a few moments, the women sat and stared in silence.

Julien's only regret was that he could also see in front of him Mme Derville, the cousin of Mme de Rênal.

'When she leaves,' he thought, 'she'll write to Mme de Rênal!'

He did not know of Mme de Rênal's arrival in Besançon.

The lawyers began their speeches – and they lasted many hours. The case against Julien, which took until the middle of the afternoon, was described almost as his own lawyer had predicted. The speeches in his defence lasted late into the evening. They seemed to go well. Too well, in fact: Julien began to feel a little angry that his lawyer was playing such an obvious game with the emotions of the women in the court. It hurt his pride. At one point Julien noticed Baron Valenod looking at him.

'That evil little man!' thought Julien. 'How he's enjoying all this!'

Julien began to think again of his life at Vergy and of the months that followed it, back in Verrières. He remembered also the bitter contempt that he had felt then for M. Valenod and all those other smart families of the town. They were all so pleased with themselves and their wealth, but lacked any real taste or any sense of true style! How they displayed their money! How hard they struggled to forget that poor families like his own ever existed!

Julien was so lost in his thoughts that only the sound of cheering all round made him realize that the lawyers' speeches had finally ended. Coffee and cakes were brought into the court. It was getting late, and many of the ladies in the courtroom had abandoned the idea of supper; they did not want to risk missing any of the trial.

The judge began his summary. He had not finished, though, when the clocks of Besançon struck midnight. This marked the end of the trial – unless the accused man wished to speak. Julien had promised his lawyer that he would say nothing; but when the judge asked him if he had anything to add, Julien stood up.

'Gentlemen of the jury,' he said, 'a horror of being pitied forces me to speak. Gentlemen, I do not have the honour of belonging to the same class as you. You see in me a peasant urged to rebel against his low position in life.

'I ask no mercy of you,' Julien continued, his voice growing stronger. 'I do not pretend to myself that all can be well; my death is waiting for me; the penalty will be fair. I have committed a horrible crime, which was entirely deliberate.

'But even if I was less than guilty, let us admit that you, the gentlemen of the jury, could never acquit me. Let us be honest. You want to make an example of me. You want to discourage any other young peasant, lucky enough to win for himself a good education, from thinking that it might be easy to mix with high society.

'That, of course, is my real crime in your eyes. And I mean all of you – not one of you knows anything of the life of a peasant family like my own. You are simply men of the middle classes who have done well for yourselves and wish to protect your positions in society ...'

There was more, much more, of the same: Julien went on speaking for another twenty minutes. He said everything that was in his heart. None of the lawyers could stop him. All the women were in floods of tears. And when Julien closed by mentioning his passion for Mme de Rênal ... Mme Derville uttered a cry and fainted to the floor.

His speech caused a sensation. None of the women had left their seats. They sat staring at this extraordinary young man who seemed not to know the most basic rules of survival. Even several of the men had tears in their eyes. It was one o'clock by the time that the jury retired to their room. At first there was plenty of excited conversation in the room; but gradually, as people grew more anxious about the return of the jury, the court grew silent.

Just as two o'clock struck, there was a sudden sound of many voices talking quickly together. The little door of the jury's room opened. Baron de Valenod advanced with more than a touch of drama in his step, followed by the rest of the jury. He coughed, then declared that the verdict of the jury was that Julien Sorel was guilty of a deliberate attempt at murder. This verdict required the death penalty; it was declared by the judge a moment later. Julien must face the guillotine. He looked at his watch; it was a quarter past two.

'Today is Friday,' was Julien's only thought.

At that moment he heard a terrible cry and was brought back to the world around him. The women on all sides were weeping;

but he saw their faces turn in the direction of a small balcony in the courtroom, built behind a stone column. There was a moment of silence. Then, as the cry was not repeated, the police sergeants stood and guided Julien out of the room.

He learnt afterwards that the balcony had been Mathilde's hiding place throughout that long day.

Chapter 12   The Final Choice

They took Julien back to a different cell in the prison – the one reserved, he soon realized, for prisoners waiting to die. He lay all night under a rough blanket, while his mind raced this way and that through the events of his life. In some strange way there seemed to be two voices in his head holding a conversation between themselves; he could not quite believe what was happening.

In the morning someone woke him with a tight grip on his shoulder.

'What, already!' said Julien, imagining it to be the call to the guillotine.

In fact it was Mathilde. He saw her changed as though by six months' illness; he could hardly recognize her.

'That cheating Frilair lied to me,' she said to him, pulling at her hands; only anger held back her tears.

'Wasn't I fine last night when I stood up to speak?' was Julien's reply. 'I was speaking straight from my heart, and for the first time in my life! I suppose it may also be the last.'

She looked at him with eyes that were red from weeping all night. There was nothing she could find to say. Julien embraced her tightly and tried to comfort her. Thoughts of Mme de Rênal, though, kept coming to his mind. He wondered: how might she have behaved in Mathilde's place?

Mathilde repeated to him in a faint voice: 'He's there, in the next room.'

Eventually Julien began to pay attention to what she was saying.

'Who is there?' he asked her gently.

'The lawyer, to help you to sign your appeal.'

'I shall not appeal.'

'What? You won't appeal?' she cried, her eyes flashing with real anger. 'And why not, if I may ask?'

'Because at this moment I feel that I have the courage to die. Who can say how I might be feeling after two months in this damp little cell? I would have to put up with endless meetings with lawyers, and with priests ... even with my father, who knows? I can imagine nothing worse ... Let me die.'

This produced a stream of abuse from Mathilde. She cursed him as angrily as she had ever done in the library of the Hôtel de la Mole. But while she poured out her anger over the next half an hour, Julien could only sit on his bed and dream about Mme de Rênal. He imagined her receiving her newspaper in her bedroom on the day after his death, and reading an account of it as she lay there in bed.

'Yes, she will cry hot tears,' he thought to himself. 'The woman whose life I tried to take will be the only one who will weep sincerely for my death!'

Failing to persuade Julien herself, Mathilde called the lawyer in. He had once been a captain in Napoleon's army, which delighted Julien. They talked for an hour of Napoleon and his battles. When at last Mathilde went away with the lawyer, Julien had a much greater feeling of friendliness for the lawyer than for her.

An hour later, as he lay sleeping, he felt tears dropping fast on his hand.

'Ah, it's Mathilde again,' he thought to himself, half awake.

'She's coming back as she promised she would, determined to make me change my mind.'

Hating the idea of another argument, he did not open his eyes. Then he heard a strange cry; he turned his head to look – and there in front of him stood Mme de Rênal.

'Ah, so I see you again before I die! Is it really you?' he cried, throwing himself at her feet. 'But forgive me, madam,' he added immediately. 'I can only be a murderer in your eyes.'

'Julien, I have come to beg you to appeal. I know you do not wish to . . .'

Her voice broke and for a moment she could say no more.

'Can you possibly forgive me?'

'If you want me to forgive you, dearest,' she said to him, embracing him in her arms, 'appeal at once against the verdict!'

Julien covered her with kisses. 'Will you come every day for two months to see me here?' he asked.

'I swear to you I will. Every day, unless my husband finds a way to prevent me.'

'Then I'll appeal!' cried Julien. 'So you do forgive me? Is it really possible?'

He held her so tightly to him that she uttered a faint cry.

'It's nothing,' she told him. 'You are hurting me.'

'It's your shoulder,' cried Julien, bursting into tears. He stepped back a little and covered her hand with burning kisses. 'Who would have predicted this, the last time I saw you, in your bedroom at Verrières?'

'Who would ever have said that I would write that shameful letter to the Marquis de la Mole?'

'Let me tell you that I have always loved you, that I have never loved anyone except you.'

'Is that really possible?' cried Mme de Rênal, overcome with joy.

She bent over Julien, who was on his knees before her, and for a long time they wept together in complete silence.

At no other time in his life had Julien experienced such a moment as this.

After a long interval, Mme de Rênal said to him: 'And that young Mlle de la Mole – what should I make of this strangely romantic story that I've heard?'

'It's only true on the surface,' replied Julien. 'She and I did plan to marry – but she is not the woman that I was meant by God to spend my life with . . .'

And so, interrupting each other a hundred times, they managed with much difficulty to tell each other of all the things that had happened to them since Julien's forced departure from Verrières. Julien told her everything about his life in Paris and with Mathilde; she told him of her life with the children – and the terrible story of how a new young priest had forced her to write that fatal letter.

Before she left, they had agreed that she would return to the prison each day. A kind soul, however, informed M. de Rênal of the long visits that his wife was making to the prison; and after three days he sent his carriage for her, with firm orders for her to return home at once.

This was a disaster for Julien. He now had to receive visits from a Mathilde who was almost mad with jealousy. She also confessed to him how she had been plotting with M. de Frilair to fix the verdict of the trial. When Julien heard of this, and of how M. Valenod had plotted against them and tricked them in the end, he turned his back finally on any thoughts of an appeal. He was sickened by everything he heard from Mathilde. His pride could not bear the thought of having to trade favours with men like M. Valenod and all the rest of them.

He had made his final choice.

◆

Just days before he was due to die, Mme de Rênal returned.

'My first duty is to you,' she said as she embraced him. 'I've run away from Verrières.'

For three days they shared every moment together that they could. To Mathilde's disgust, Mme de Rênal somehow managed (with a large amount of money) to bribe the guards into allowing her to see Julien at any time. The two of them lived with hardly a thought about the future. When Mme de Rênal mentioned the possibility that she could appeal to the King in Paris, Julien told her he would certainly kill himself if she did so. After that the subject of an appeal was never discussed again.

Julien was finding the smell of his cell hard to bear by the day on which he had to die. Fortunately there was a bright sun that morning, and he was in the mood to feel brave. To step out into the open air was a delight for him, as the first steps on dry land are for a sailor who has been at sea.

'Good,' he said to himself, 'everything is going well ... My courage isn't failing me.'

His head had never looked more handsome than at the moment before it fell. The sweetest moments he had known in the past, walking in the woods of Vergy, came rushing back into his mind in every detail.

Everything passed simply and decently, with no trace of theatre or pretence by Julien. The guillotine did its job.

Some days before, he had made arrangements for Fouqué to carry off both Mathilde and Mme de Rênal in his carriage at full speed on the morning of his death.

'They may fight or they may fall into each other's arms,' he had told Fouqué, 'but at least the poor women will have their minds slightly taken off their terrible grief.'

He had also obtained a solid promise from Mme de Rênal that she would never consider killing herself but would live to watch over Mathilde's child.

Fouqué did as he had promised in this sad bargain.

Later, he was spending the night alone in his house, beside the body of his friend, when, to his great surprise, he saw Mathilde appear at the door. A few hours earlier he had left her a short ride from Besançon. Her face was wild, her eyes were on fire.

'I want to see him,' she said.

Fouqué had not the courage either to speak or to rise from his chair. He pointed with his finger to a great blue blanket on the floor; in it was wrapped all that remained of Julien.

She threw herself on her knees. The memory of Boniface de la Mole must have given her unnatural courage. With trembling hands she opened up the blanket. Fouqué turned his eyes away.

He heard Mathilde walking quickly about the room. She was lighting a number of candles. When he forced himself to turn around and look at her, she had placed Julien's head in front of her on a low table and was kissing his forehead ...

◆

Next day a large number of priests set off from the house with Julien's remains, and took them almost as far as Verrières. There they left the road and climbed a small track up the side of the mountain on the outskirts of the town, to the little cave near the top where Julien had more than once spent the night. He had asked Fouqué to make sure that he was buried in the cave, and it was completely dark by the time the burial party arrived there.

Mathilde followed them. Sitting all alone in her carriage covered in black cloth, she carried on her knees, unknown to anyone, the head of the man she had loved so passionately.

Inside the cave, hundreds of candles were set down and they lit up a scene of extraordinary drama. Just outside stood a great crowd of people from the little mountain villages through which the burial party had travelled.

Mathilde appeared in the middle of them, in long funeral

85

clothes that fell down to her feet; and at the end of the service, she arranged for several thousands of francs to be scattered among the villagers.

Left alone with Fouqué, she insisted on burying her lover's head in the ground with her own hands. Fouqué went nearly mad with grief.

To show how much she had loved him, Mathilde later arranged for the bare cave to be decorated with beautiful polished stones, shaped at great cost in Italy.

Mme de Rênal was loyal to her promise, too. She did not attempt to take her own life; but three days after Julien's death, she gave each of her children a last embrace, and died.

ACTIVITIES

Chapters 1–3

Before you read

1 Julien Sorel is an eighteen-year-old who loves books, but his father is a carpenter who cannot read. How could this have happened? What do you think the consequences have been for Julien?

2 Find the words in *italics* in your dictionary. They are all in the story.
   a Discuss possible connections between these words.
   heir and *francs*
   passion, tutor and *seduce*
   scandal and *guillotine*
   b Describe the colour *scarlet*.

After you read

3 How does Stendhal suggest that M. de Rênal is not a strong character? How has M. de Rênal nevertheless succeeded in becoming Mayor of Verrières, do you think?

4 Work in pairs. Have this conversation. Imagine you are business rivals of the Mayor in Verrières, discussing the two roles played by Julien on the day of the King's visit. What do you think about his involvement? What do you think is going to happen in the de Rênal household?

Chapters 4–6

Before you read

5 How do you think the Mayor will react to the unsigned letter? Do you think that Julien is in danger, or will Mme de Rênal try to find a way to help him and continue with their relationship?

6 Find the words in *italics* in your dictionary.
   a Act out these verbs.
   embrace   flirt   weep
   b Use these words to complete the sentences.
   aristocracy   clergy   despair   duel   pistol   poison-pen
   Rector   seminary   shutters

87

He felt ..... when he received a ..... letter about his wife's behaviour.

He loaded his ..... to fight a ..... at dawn.

The head of a ..... is called the ..... . Most members of the ..... were trained there.

She opened the ..... to let light into the room.

Many members of the French ..... were killed in the Revolution.

After you read

7 Mme de Rênal can always guess how her husband will react to events. How does she use this understanding of her husband's character to make sure that Julien comes to no harm?

8 When Julien returns to visit Mme de Rênal, she tries to hide him from the servants. Do you think that she succeeds? Why does M. de Rênal eventually decide that there are burglars in the house?

Chapters 7–9

Before you read

9 What do you think will be the biggest challenges that Julien will face in Paris? Do you believe he will be happy living there?

10 Find these words in your dictionary.

Baron   contempt   Count   drawing room   execute

Which are words for

a a place?

b a feeling?

c an action?

d people?

After you read

11 Who

a takes Julien around the great houses of London?

b are the Moustaches?

c was guillotined in 1574?

d asks to be introduced by Julien to the Marquis?

e makes Mathilde de la Mole violently jealous?

12 What interests and opinions do Julien and Mathilde share? In what ways do they also have quite similar personalities?

13 Do you think that Prince Korasoff's approach to romantic relationships would still work in the modern world – or is Stendhal telling a story that could not happen today?

Chapters 10–12

Before you read

14 How do you think that the Marquis will react to the news in Mathilde's letter? What will he do?

15 How do you think that Mme de Rênal will react if she hears that Julien is going to be married in Paris?

16 Find these words in your dictionary.

acquit   cavalry   Lieutenant   regiment   verdict

Which words are connected with

a military affairs?

b legal matters?

After you read

17 Who says these words? Who to?

a 'It was your duty to go ...'

b 'You won't find me a coward!'

c 'This young man has everything except youth.'

d 'Please understand my position.'

e 'My first duty is to you.'

18 Discuss these questions.

a What is Mathilde's first reaction to the news from Verrières?

b Who reveals to Mathilde the full story about Julien and Mme de Rênal, and why?

c Why does Julien make such an unexpected speech at the trial?

d Should Mme de Rênal have tried harder to persuade Julien to appeal against his verdict? Do you think she might have succeeded?

Writing

19 Write your own version of the important messages about Julien that are sent in the first letters
   a from M. Valenod to M. de Rênal;
   b from Father Chélan to Father Pirard;
   c from the Marquis de la Mole to his daughter;
   d from Mme de Rênal to the Marquis.
20 What is the significance in Julien's life of these three colours, and what they represent?
   a scarlet   b black   c blue
21 How do these characters all cause dramatic changes in Julien's career?
   Elisa   M. de Frilair   Mme Fervaques
22 What do the different reactions of Mathilde and Mme de Rênal at the end of the story tell you about their characters?
23 You are the judge at Julien's trial. Write down your summary of the case and the reasons why you decided to confirm the verdict of the jury.
24 Imagine you are a journalist on the local Verrières newspaper, reporting on the death of Mme de Rênal. Give an account of her last few weeks and explain briefly the story behind them.